OLD DOG LOVE

Dr Joanna de Klerk

Publication Data

Dr Joanna de Klerk

Old Dog Love --- First edition.

Summary: "Ensuring your senior dog lives a happy, healthy, and fulfilling life" --- Provided by publisher.

ISBN: 978-1-952069-02-4

[1. Old Dog Love --- Non-Fiction] I. Title.

This book has been written with the published intent to provide accurate and authoritative information in regard to the subject matter included. While every reasonable precaution has been taken in preparation of this book the author and publisher expressly disclaim responsibility for any errors, omissions, or adverse effects arising from the use or application of the information contained inside. The techniques and suggestions are to be used at the reader's discretion and are not to be considered a substitute for professional veterinary care. If you suspect a medical problem with your dog, consult your veterinarian.

Design by Sorin Rădulescu

First paperback edition, 2020

TABLE OF CONTENTS

Preface

When I started my career as a vet in rural Southern England, I began to see a large percentage of old, creaky Labradors (because everyone loves a Lab in the country!). They often came in with a tight expression and staring eyes. Their soft, loving natures were telling them not to complain, but the reality was, they were battling with great discomfort. The Labrador breed is prone to arthritis in older age, and I wished that I could help the dogs more than just pulling a bottle of anti-inflammatories from the shelf in the hope that it would suppress the pain enough to improve their quality of life.

By the time I had been in practice for a couple of years, I knew I needed to learn more. I proceeded to study Western Acupuncture, then a few years later, a Certificate in Companion Animal Pain Management. The new knowledge I acquired was life changing, and enabled me to be able to provide a much more holistic approach to senior dog care and pain management.

In early 2019, I ended up opening my own veterinary facility, focusing on pain management and rehabilitation. Day in and day out, I saw many senior dogs come through my doors with mobility issues, but often other ailments too. I heard continuously "it's just his age," but the reality is, age is only a number. Age is not a disease, it's a life-stage, and I have to constantly remind my clients of that. Sure, the aging body is prone to more ailments, but with diligent senior dog care, many dogs can live well into their mid and even late teens. With that being said, I always advocate quality over quantity when it comes to life, but it is certainly possible to have both a quality life and a long life.

When given the opportunity to write this book on senior dog care, I was excited at the prospect of being able to put down in writing all of my top tips for having a happy, healthy, long-living dog. Having owned several senior dogs throughout my lifetime, I've learned about senior dog care from a first-hand perspective, as well as from the other side of the consulting table. The current dogs in my life are 12 and 14 years old, and you'd have no idea when you see them leap about on their daily walks.

Senior dog care requires more than just a change in healthcare. Nutrition, grooming, dental care, home enrichment and exercise all play a role in keeping your senior dog in top shape and these are up to you to address at home. So, I hope this book can provide you with plenty of encouragement, ideas and information about how to enrich the senior years of your dog, maintain his general well-being, and teach you about senior ailments, so that you are prepared to journey through your old friend's senior years with him, come what may.

CHAPTER 1
How Old is Old?

Photo Courtesy of Maggie Estby

Dogs have evolved and been bred into a myriad of different forms since their earliest common ancestor. As a result, there is no single age that can be considered senior when it comes to dogs. In terms of lifespan, some breeds of dog will live happily into their late teens and others may only expect to live 7 years. The point at which a dog is considered senior is also variable, and does not necessarily correspond to lifespan, as certain breeds are genetically healthier than others, and some dogs have the advantage of optimum healthcare from puppyhood, which will increase their healthy years.

Nevertheless, as a general rule, most vets consider a medium-sized dog to be senior from around the age of 7. At this point in your dog's life, you may begin to notice some of the telltale signs of aging. Some dogs may simply slow down. This may be due to a slump in their metabolism, also causing weight to creep on. As well as a bit of middle age spread, you may also notice some graying of the muzzle. Or dogs may begin to suffer stiffness after a walk or trouble getting up the stairs.

Just like us in our senior years, dogs can experience a gradual loss of sight, hearing, and even cognitive function. For some dogs, these changes cause anxiety; and your dog might not like things being changed around in the home or deal well with day-to-day stress factors. If you have had your dog from a young age, you will know him well, and be sensitive to a change in his demeanor that is telling you he needs a different approach. This book is intended to help you spot these signs and act on them in good time, so that your dog can enjoy his senior years to the fullest.

Photo Courtesy of
Kate Evenson

The Differences in Dog Breeds

Whether you have a dog that can expect to live to 7 or 17 depends very much on his breed. Within each breed, the expected lifespan is quite specific, usually to within 2 years. For a dog to live less or more than this, there is usually a causative factor. Some of these may be down to care, and others simply good or bad luck. But looking at the more general picture, there is a correlation between breed size and lifespan.

Small Breeds

Small breeds can generally look forward to a long lifespan. For example, terriers will often live into their mid to late teens. Most terrier breeds were bred to be hardy little working dogs, so they are also usually very healthy well into their senior years. Other small pedigree dogs can also fare well in terms of life expectancy, as long as they haven't suffered the genetic effects of irresponsible breeding. The Maltese, Shih Tzu, Lhasa Apso, Toy Poodle and Chihuahua are amongst the longest living dog breeds. Small breeds usually settle well into their senior years, as they need less exercise than larger dogs, so will happily adapt to a more sedentary life.

Photo Courtesy of Deborah Cox

. As a very approximate average, your small dog may expect to live to 14 years, and is senior at 9.

Large Breeds

Photo Courtesy of Andria Bertucci

The Great Dane is commonly used as an example of a large dog with a short lifespan of around seven years. Large breed dogs are often more susceptible to heart and joint problems and should be carefully managed during the rapid growth of their puppy years. Large breeds need a lot of exercise during their earlier years, so if they begin to experience joint problems, they may not adapt so well to slowing down. However, controlled exercise is still important as their metabolism becomes sluggish, as excessive weight gain will put added strain on their joints and vital organs. Exercise also fulfills an important role in a dog's mental wellbeing.

As a very approximate average, your large dog may expect to live to 10 years and will be a senior at 6.

FUN FACT
World's Oldest Dog

According to the Guinness Book of World Records, the oldest recorded dog was an Australian cattle dog named Bluey who lived to be 29 years and five months old. Bluey worked with sheep and cattle in Rochester, Victoria, Australia, until his death in November 1939.

Crossbreeds

Crossbreeds can be affected by the same hereditary diseases that are common in their pedigree component parts. However, their overall greater genetic diversity usually offers a protective effect. This advantage is known as "hybrid vigor." A recent study showed that whereas purebred dogs can expect to live to an average 11.9 years, crossbred dogs average 13.1 years (O'Neill, D.G., et al, Longevity and Mortality of Owned Dogs in England. The Veterinary Journal, 2013, 198(3). p.638-643). And, because crossbreeds gen-

Photo Courtesy of John Sieber

erally benefit from fewer inherited conditions, they are likely to stay fitter and healthier in their senior years.

Since crossbreeds cover such a diversity of sizes and breeds in their genetic mix, their lifespan average of 13 years will represent the greatest range, from perhaps 8 to 20 years. And out of all breeds, they may enjoy the longest number of years sporting the grizzly senior look.

Finances

Your dog's senior years are likely to be more costly than those before, and these expenses are mostly health-related.

As well as becoming a more regular visitor at the veterinary clinic, your senior dog requires a special diet that may be more expensive than what he was eating before.

Because of this well-known fact, if you are adopting a senior dog, your financial situation is likely to be assessed by the rescue to be sure that you can afford it. Rather than adoption, some rescues will only foster out senior dogs, remaining responsible for their healthcare for life.

Investing For the Future

Photo Courtesy of
Alexandria Schubring

If you have had your dog from an early age, you will have been able to give him a head start in his senior health by managing his exercise, providing a good quality diet, and ensuring he has had regular veterinary checks throughout his life. You may also have started him on joint supplements before any visible signs of arthritis. In fact, even at the very start, you may have paid more for a healthy dog from a responsible, registered breeder. These precautions could reduce any major expenses as your dog enters his senior years and represent a sensible investment in his future.

Insurance

Photo Courtesy of Stacey Osburn

Not all insurers will accept new policies for older dogs. However, if you insured your dog from a young age under a policy that covers him for life, you will be able to continue with this coverage.

It is important to realize that after a certain age, most insurers will dramatically increase the premium you pay to insure your senior dog. You will also find that the excess you pay and the percentage of the claim has increased. So, you should always look at your renewal proposal to assess whether your insurance coverage is still worthwhile. For dogs who are on medication for a long-term condition, you can do the math to see whether your coverage is still a viable proposition. If you change insurers, any pre-existing conditions will not be covered.

It is worth bearing in mind that the highest veterinary bills you may encounter are associated with surgical operations. As your senior dog will have a lower chance of a good surgical outcome at this time of life, you may decide you don't want to put him through invasive treatment. Sometimes, having access to insurance may not even be in the dog's best interest, when an owner is encouraged to max out their coverage by persisting with treatments that are only prolonging the length, and not the quality, of their dog's life.

On the other hand, if you can afford the higher premiums, pet insurance for your senior dog allows you to manage your budget, as well as ensuring any decisions you make for your dog are not determined by finance alone.

HELPFUL TIP
Read the Fine Print

Pet insurance comes in a variety of formats and it's important to read the fine print so you know exactly what you're getting. While some pet insurance plans cover preventative and routine care, some only cover your pet if it has been in an accident or has ingested a hazardous substance. It's also important to note what kind of waiting periods and payout limits your pet insurance may impose.

Photo Courtesy of
Adena Glebus

These are all things to consider in deciding whether to continue with your dog's insurance, or to self-fund his health care during his senior years.

If you decide to self-fund, you should take your dog for a full check-up, including blood and urine analysis, before canceling your insurance policy, so there are no hidden surprises. You should then be disciplined in putting aside the money you would have paid in premiums, so that any medical expenses don't catch you unawares.

Expectations

Your dog's senior years will usually be the most settled of your time together, as you both know each other and have a routine. Your dog is trained, and your expectations of each other are well established, so communication between you is second nature, and your dog really has become a best friend.

On the other hand, if you have adopted a senior dog, you will just be getting to know each other, and you may be dealing with some undesirable ingrained behaviors from lack of early training or bad experiences. However, these should have been flagged by the rescue during the assessment process, so you are aware of the challenges ahead. Most rescues will also offer behavioral support if need-ed. And those who take on a se-nior rescue dog do so for the sat-isfaction of ensuring the quality of their twilight years makes up for their past.

Although senior dogs are generally quieter and easi-er to live with than an exuber-ant youngster, during this peri-od, your dog is experiencing the physical effects of aging, which may cause you some extra work and extra consideration of how he can best manage his daily life.

Because of the bond that has built up between you over the years, or your commitment to your new rescue dog, these small sacrifices are usually car-ried out with love and tolerance, and it's worth remembering that your dog is not at fault and does not want to exasperate you. Because older dogs can be easily stressed by their physical failings and by displeasing you, every owner should be patient, understanding, and have some idea of what to ex-pect in the coming years.

Senior Dogs in the House

Photo Courtesy of
Chelsea Sedlak

In many ways, senior dogs are a lot less trouble around the house than they may have been in their destructive puppy years. They now have a favorite bed and a favorite toy, and no lon-ger shred the furniture or chew the TV remote. They know that the place to potty is outside, that when you go out you come back, and they have a routine that keeps both of you happy.

By now, you have settled on whether your dog is allowed on the couch or upstairs, and whether he is allowed in the bedrooms, or sleeps there or

Photo Courtesy of
John Sieber

downstairs. Everyone knows the house rules, and your dog respects your boundaries, even finding them reassuring.

(If you have adopted a senior dog, you may not be experiencing such a quiet life, but in Chapter 2 you will find some tips on how to help your dog settle in.)

However, your senior dog may now be facing the challenge of losing physical control over some of his bodily functions, especially pottying. If your house-trained dog starts to urinate or defecate in the house, it does not necessarily mean he has regressed with his training, although it may be a part of cognitive decline. But more often it's due to a physical laxity that means he cannot hold back when he needs to void. This is especially common in spayed females, who often lose the tone in their urinary sphincter in later life, but your vet can prescribe medication to help with this problem. If your dog is experiencing incontinence, you just need to take him outside more, even during the night, and avoid leaving him alone for long periods. Incontinence in the older dog is discussed further in Chapter 3.

Pottying indoors can also indicate that your dog is stressed. Anxiety is common in older dogs, as they may be losing their vision and hearing. Displeasing you will also add to their stress if you overreact to an accident in the house. Dogs suffering from stress often like to have a cozy den made for them in a corner of their favorite room. Other home remedies for anxiety include pheromone (DAP) diffusers, and Thundershirts. But your vet may also prescribe medication if the problem is severe.

Due to the onset of arthritis, your senior dog may be experiencing problems getting on and off the couch or the bed, if he is allowed to do so. What's more, jumping on and off furniture can damage elderly joints. Consider doggy steps, which can be purchased from a pet store or online, or simply place some sturdy blocks against the furniture to do the same job. Your dog may need to be taught how to use them, but should soon get the idea.

If your pet struggles with the stairs, tackling them alone may put undue strain on his joints, so you may consider installing a stair gate at the top and bottom. This way you can carry him up and down the stairs when he wants to use them, or at least steady his movements. If your dog is too big to carry, he may need to adapt to sleeping downstairs. A cozy orthopedic bed and his favorite toys will help ease the transition. Arthritis in the older dog is discussed further in Chapter 6.

Senior Dogs Out and About

Exercise has always been an important part of your dog's daily routine, and should continue to be so in his old age, both for his physical and mental health.

Photo Courtesy of Chelsea Schoof

Photo Courtesy of Bonnie Burns

However, once your dog starts to feel his age, with lower energy levels and creaky joints, you will notice him slowing down, and perhaps looking very stiff after his walks. This is a sign that he needs to ease up on the intensity and duration of his walks as he enters his senior years.

Most dogs will settle for a daily routine of gentler physical exercise in their senior years, although for very active dogs there may still be a tendency to overdo it. Some owners find joint supplements very effective in easing their dog's discomfort. These can take the form of nutraceuticals such as green lipped mussel, glucosamine, chondroitin, MSM or turmeric. Or the vet can prescribe anti-inflammatories, however these can take a toll on the liver of senior dogs if taken on a regular basis.

If you and your dog have been used to long country walks in all weather, it can be just as much of an adjustment for you as for your dog when he can no longer keep up and feels the effect of the cold more than he used to. Now your walks need to prioritize quality over quantity – maybe you can take the car to the best part of a favorite park. And be sure to have a towel in the car to dry your dog off before the cold sets in. Older dogs feel the cold more keenly than they used to, and it can make their stiffness worse, so your dog may benefit from a coat in cold or wet weather.

You may also need to carry a leash for use at any point your dog might forget his years and tear off with no thought of the consequences! You may also find you are using the leash more in your dog's senior years if he is suffering from a loss of vision or hearing.

Older dogs should be discouraged from jumping into or out of the car, so a portable folding ramp is a worthwhile purchase that will also save you lifting a heavy, soggy dog.

It can be difficult if you still have a younger dog as well as your senior, as both have different exercise requirements. If you have someone else with you, this may be possible to manage at a single location where you can take different routes. But if you are managing alone, your younger dog may just require an extra walk while your senior takes a nap at home later in the day.

Photo Courtesy of Studio Twelve: 52 Owner – Stephanie Hyser

Be aware that your senior dog may be less tolerant of the unwanted attentions of other dogs when you are out and about, so you may wish to create a diversion if you see a lively puppy approaching. If your dog really cannot cope with other dogs, he can wear a harness or leash with the message "I need space." These are widely available, and encourage other owners to control their dog near yours.

If your senior dog is experiencing hindlimb weakness, some owners find that their dog can still enjoy a gentle walk supported by a sling around the hind quarters. These are widely available. If the problem becomes more severe, some owners may invest in a dog wheelchair, which is a wheeled aluminum frame that takes the weight off the hind legs while propulsion is made by the forelegs. Or small dogs may still enjoy the fresh air from the vantage point of a stroller or pet carrier. When your dog reaches this stage, however, it may be time to start considering his quality of life.

Quality of Life

What is It?

The most important consideration for any dog owner, especially as their best friend reaches his senior years, is an appreciation of his quality of life. "Quality of life" is a saying that most vets bring up when assessing how joyous or suffering a dog's life is.

When you have taken the utmost care of your dog all his life and only ever given him the best, it can be hard to accept that he might not have any joy in his life any more. But this is almost always due to the natural process of physical decline, and not due to any shortcoming in you as his owner and provider. It is important to step back and be objective when you consider your dog's quality of life, as the one gift we can give our dogs at the end is a dignified and peaceful departure before their pain turns into suffering.

Photo Courtesy of
Debbie & Michael Seybert

How to Judge It?

Some dogs cope stoically with degenerative diseases for many of their senior years, especially as so many conditions can be managed with the right diet and medication. So, the most reliable way to assess your dog's quality of life is to look for changes in his demeanor.

Dogs can be very expressive with their emotions. Happiness and sadness are very easy to recognize. More subtle signs that they are struggling however may be seen in their activity level, and especially in their appetite. When a dog is lethargic for a long time, or when he starts to refuse even the most appetizing food, it probably indicates that age and illness

Photo Courtesy of Nick Schanilec

are catching up with him. The point at which you have to hand feed your dog on a daily basis is the point when your dog may be saying he has had enough, and it is time to let go. For some owners this can be very hard to accept, especially if their pet has not attained the average lifespan for his breed. However, it's important to realize that a dog lives in the moment, with no concept of how many years he should have, only that those years were happy and free of pain or suffering. A well-known phrase sums it up, "Better a week too early than a day too late."

For most owners who know their dogs well, they will simply see in their eyes when the time has come. If you have any doubt in your own judgement, you should trust your vet's experience, as they have taken an oath always to act in the best interest of the animals entrusted to them.

Saying goodbye is discussed in greater depth in Chapter 7.

CHAPTER 2
Adopting a Senior Dog

Whereas most owners of dogs entering their senior years have also journeyed with them through their puppy and adult life-stages, for many people, their senior dog is a newcomer to the family. This is usually as a result of adoption from an animal shelter, but can also be due to a death in the family or a private rehoming arrangement.

Photo Courtesy of
Sophie Werner

Photo Courtesy of
Domineeque Provident

Benefits of an Older Dog

There are many benefits of adopting an older dog that make this a good choice for certain people. The most obvious advantage is that a senior dog is likely to be a much quieter member of the family than a puppy, and in most cases, will come already house broken with some training in place. It's also a plus factor if a dog already has reasonable recall. Of course, a lot of rescue dogs have not had such a good start, and there is a saying, "You can't teach an old dog new tricks." This means any shortcomings in a dog's obedience at the senior stage will be harder to correct than they would be with a puppy. But for many people who choose to adopt, part of the satisfaction is in rising to the challenge and building a bond with the dog whose life they hope to change for the better.

For those who are entering their senior years themselves, adopting an older dog makes a lot of sense. Many potential adopters have a wealth of experience behind them in caring for dogs in the past, so are well equipped to take on a new friend who may have health needs over the coming years. There is also the lifespan consideration, as the average dog will live 10-14 years, and potential owners in their retirement years may not feel they can guarantee their own health so far into the future. In taking on a dog who has fewer years left to him on the clock, they may feel more comfortable with the commitment.

It may seem a harsh thing to have to consider, but many rescue organizations will not rehome puppies to applicants in their later years. However, they will gladly partner older individuals with a senior dog in need of a quiet, loving home. In fact, the match is usually best all around, as senior dogs faced with settling into a new home may not cope so well in a busy family environment, so a mature owner, with whom they can form a simple bond, is just what they need at their time of life.

Photo Courtesy of
Sarah Jones

Personality

Every breed has its own specific character traits, and unlike with a puppy, the personality of a senior dog is developed. So, you know roughly what you are getting when you take on a senior.

As a broad generalization, a senior dog adopted from a shelter will usually have a more mellow character than a young dog. But of course, the circumstances that have led to a rescue dog being in a shelter may have been damaging, and he may be dealing with some behavioral issues. These may be due to lack of training in his earlier years, or psychological damage from cruelty, or simply from separation from the people he previously saw as his own.

When a dog is taken in by a rescue organization, he will always be fully assessed. Quite often, he will go into a foster home under the management of the rescue, to see how he behaves in a home environment, and whether he can live with children and other pets. Otherwise, the rescue will assess him at the center, sometimes with the help of a professional behaviorist. So, when you adopt a dog from a shelter, you should always be given an overview of his personality traits. This is just as important to the rescue as it is for the adopter, as it is in everyone's best interests, and especially the dog's, if the adoption works out the first time. It is never good for a dog to be rehomed multiple times, as each time the bond he has begun to form is destroyed, this damages his trust, and makes for a more anxious dog.

The rescue will make sure you are a good match for the dog that you hope to adopt by asking a lot of questions. Sometimes a rescue will send someone out to visit your house to assess whether it's suitable for the dog. A home check is never about having an expensive, immaculate house. It is simply to check that you live where you say you do, that you have permission to keep a dog if your home is rented, that your home is hygienic but not so pristine that a dog's hair, slobber, and dirt would be an issue, and that there is sufficient space and a safely enclosed yard.

Being thoroughly checked out by the rescue is a good sign and not to be resented, as it shows the organization is working to ensure a successful partnership. The ASPCA says, "We believe in matching people and pets through dialogue and conversation, in a climate of trust and communication."

You will not fail a home check for any rectifiable shortcomings. But these will be flagged by the home checker, for example, a missing fence panel, so that you can address them before bringing your dog home.

When it comes to senior dogs, some rescues will only foster out, and adoption will not be offered. This allows the rescue organization greater control over the dog's care, and is usually due to ongoing health needs. The

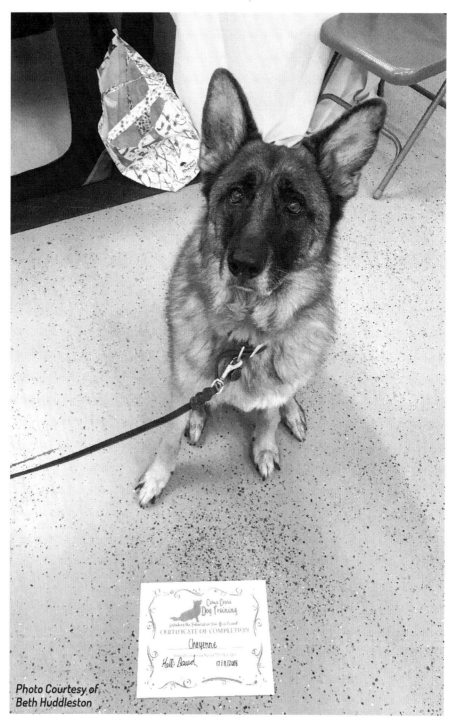

Photo Courtesy of
Beth Huddleston

advantage of this arrangement is that it reduces the financial burden on you, but the disadvantage is that it may seem like your dog is not your own. Technically, a rescue dog is never your own even if adopted, as most adoption agreements require you to return the dog to the rescue if your circumstances change, and never rehome it privately. This is simply in the best interest of the dog, and in practice, most people who adopt a rescue dog feel it is theirs, and any further interaction with the rescue is a voluntary sharing of news and photos to say how well the dog is doing!

You should be prepared for the fact that however thoroughly the rescue organization has assessed the personality of your chosen dog, this can change once he comes home with you. Although most dogs adapt well, it can take time for a rescue dog to settle, so patience and a willingness to work with the dog are both important. The shelter will usually provide support and advice, and may be able to put you in touch with a behaviorist if you need extra help.

Training and Housebreaking

As previously mentioned, one advantage to adopting a senior dog is that the work of training and housebreaking may have already been done for you. And even if the dog has come into care lacking in these skills, most rescues will work to housebreak the dog and establish some basic training before rehoming him. It will then be important to keep the training going, as older dogs can be slower to learn new skills and more prone to regression.

Apart from rescue dogs, other seniors may need to learn how to live in a house. These are retired working dogs or yard dogs, which have lived previously in a kennel or yard, but have been brought inside to spend their final years in a warm environment.

You can use all the same training techniques with a senior dog that you would with a puppy. Reward-based training is the way to go with any dog, and particularly with a senior who is feeling unsettled, as what he needs is love and encouragement. Harsh training methods or punishing an older rescue dog will be hugely detrimental, as he already feels insecure. It

HELPFUL TIP
Belly Bands

House-training can be a tricky endeavor whether you're training a puppy or dealing with an older dog's incontinence. Dog diapers and belly bands are an excellent way to minimize cleanup and discourage pets from marking. These options are especially beneficial for keeping your senior dog clean, dry, and comfortable during bouts of incontinence. Both belly bands and dog diapers come in a variety of sizes and in reusable cloth or disposable plastic.

will lead to anxiety, which can cause unwanted vocalization and even incontinence. So, patience, consistency, and positive reinforcement will show your dog the ropes. It is in a dog's nature to want to please you!

If, when you bring your senior rescue dog home, you find that he messes in the house, don't panic! He has had a lot of changes in his life recently, and settling in always takes time. Physically, he may not have as good muscle tone as a younger dog, so may be more prone to messing if he is stressed or if he has not had a recent opportunity to potty outdoors. The answer is to take your dog out frequently, and when he moves into position to potty, use a command word, such as "Busy," then make a big fuss of him for being such a good boy! Eventually he will associate the word with the action, so you can tell him to potty on command.

You can also use treats to reward your dog when you are training him, but be aware that senior dogs have a slower metabolism and are prone to weight gain. So, keep the treats small and adjust your dog's food ration accordingly.

Some dogs, especially spayed females, develop urinary incontinence in old age. Also, some medical conditions can affect bladder and bowel control. If housebreaking does not go to plan, you should see your vet. Often, medication or a change of diet may resolve the problem.

Just because your dog is older, doesn't mean you can't go to local dog training classes. These can be a great way to benefit from professional expertise and moral support. Most dogs will enjoy the opportunity to meet other dogs at training classes, however for some seniors; it can be too much, especially if there are a lot of boisterous puppies in the class. Some classes will separate the older dogs if there are enough of them, which your dog may prefer. If classes don't work out for your dog however, there are some excellent training tutorials online.

Many senior dogs are content just to potter around and sniff on their walks, and never go far from your side. For some rescue dogs though, being off-leash is just the opportunity they need to bolt off with no intention of coming back. After all, he doesn't know you properly yet, and he may even have trust issues with humans in general. If you are experiencing a lack of reliable recall with your senior rescue dog, it is not too late to train him.

Keep a handful of small treats in your pocket, or better still, a plastic box that rattles, and choose a secure area or use an extra-long training line on your dog. Gain his attention, then send him away with the "Free" command. If you are using a training line, you can then gently pull to encourage him back with the "Come" command, and treat him when he returns to your side. If you are not using a line, but are just in a secure area, wait until your dog naturally makes eye contact with you, then encourage him back, only using "Come" when he is actively coming to you. Give him a treat or some fuss, then send him away again. Changing direction is an excellent way of maintaining your dog's focus on you. Keep up the repetition, but if he loses attention, it's time to stop the session for that day.

Some dogs are simply not motivated by food, but are more responsive to a toy or ball. So, use whatever works for your dog, but praise always reinforces a correct action!

Reducing Shelter Crowding

Older dogs are often overlooked at shelters, as most adopters are looking for a young, fit dog with many years ahead of them. Consequently, an older dog may spend more time at the shelter waiting for a new owner, which can be detrimental to his physical and mental health. For this reason, many shelters will make a special effort to place seniors in foster care while they wait.

The ASPCA has a proactive approach to rehoming older dogs, advising rescue organizations to provide full physicals on seniors in their care, including blood work, urinalysis, vaccinations, heartworm testing, dentals, and mass removals if required. They also suggest reducing or waiving the adoption fee on older dogs, being totally transparent about the dog's medical and behavioral needs, and providing full support and sharing of resources.

For an adopter who is particularly motivated by compassionate reasons, choosing an older dog brings special satisfaction, as they know that they are offering a home to a dog in the greatest need. This can create a really strong bond between both parties.

FUN FACT
The Oldest Shelter in America

The Morris Animal Refuge in Philadelphia is the oldest animal shelter in America. Founder Elizabeth Morris began sheltering animals in her home in 1858. In 1874 the Morris Animal Refuge was founded in a small house on 10th Street. The shelter moved to its current location in 1878 and continues to operate as an open admission shelter that has never turned an animal away.
Website:
https://www.morrisanimalrefuge.org

If you are a potential adopter with the financial security to take on a senior dog whose health needs may be greater, and if you are not concerned with the number of years you may have together, then choosing senior may be the most rewarding thing you ever do.

Considerations When Adopting

There are a few additional considerations worth weighing up when you are thinking of adopting an oldie.

Unknown Health Ailments

Dogs that find themselves in a shelter usually come with no pedigree. Or if they do have pedigree papers, these are usually not passed on by the rescue organization, to prevent unscrupulous profiteering from the resale of the adopted dog. The abuse of pedigree papers for breeding from a rescue dog is not usually an issue, as most dogs are neutered when they come into rescue, even in their senior years. However, some older dogs will not be suitable candidates for anesthesia or surgery, so occasionally a shelter will have to rehome an intact dog, but the adoption agreement will carry a condition that the dog must not be used for breeding.

Because shelter dogs usually come with unknown parentage and an unknown history, you are unlikely to know whether your dog has any inherited conditions that are yet to make themselves known. With orthope-

Photo Courtesy of
Marnie Harrell
Shadymist Kennel

Photo Courtesy of
Jennifer Swantz

dic conditions, such as hip dysplasia or patella luxation, a veterinary check should pick these up even if they are not already causing problems. Your vet should also be able to spot any weaknesses due to previous injuries. But some genetic predispositions, such as cancers, may only appear late in life, and some conditions, such as seizures, are intermittent, therefore may not have been picked up while the dog was at the shelter.

On the plus side, with an unknown history, if you are able to find a pet insurer willing to cover your senior dog, you will have no pre-existing conditions to declare, therefore no automatic exclusions.

Getting Along with Family and Other Pets

When the shelter has approved your application, you have passed a home check, and been paired up with a suitable dog, you may be offered a "Meet-and-Greet" session, where your dog can meet other members of the family, in particular any other dogs that share your home.

This initial meeting is only a rough indicator of how things may go in the longer term, as meeting casually in a neutral environment is quite a different thing to sharing a living space 24 hours a day. However, it is a useful test of how well your new rescue dog reacts and how you should prepare for his homecoming.

Your new dog will have been assessed by the rescue, and will not be placed in a home with other dogs or children if he has demonstrated any

HELPFUL TIP

Is a Trial Run Right for You?

Animal shelters are increasingly offering a trial period or "sleepover" option for prospective adopting families. This can be a great way to test a potential pet's compatibility with your family and current pets. Something to keep in mind if you opt for a trial run with a new dog: the transition from shelter to home life may be stressful and overwhelming for a dog. Some experts say that it can take weeks for a dog to adjust and become comfortable in new surroundings.

aggression with either. However, dogs that find themselves living alongside each other can often scrap during the settling in period. This is sometimes to establish the pecking order, but can just be play-fighting. You should observe both dogs' body language for any signs of true aggression, such as stiffness, lips drawn back, and a rapidly vibrating tail, and separate them before either oversteps the mark. Senior dogs have less patience than they did in their younger days, and the constant attentions of a young dog may become tiresome to them, leading them to snap. Most dogs sort things out between themselves in due course.

Rescues are acutely aware of their liabilities if they should place an aggressive dog in a home with children that should lead to the child being bitten. Therefore, many dogs will not be made available to young families, and those that are will have been thoroughly assessed. All the same, the relationship your child has with your new dog depends less on training the dog and more on training the child.

If your child has no previous experience of living with dogs, you should take them to visit other people's child-friendly dogs in the run-up to bringing your new dog home, and show them how to approach and stroke a dog. You should make sure they understand never to startle a dog, or to fuss over it when it is eating or sleeping. You should show them where the dog will enjoy being stroked, on the back of its neck and back, and where they should leave well alone, around the eyes and mouth. And you should make quite sure they understand the dog isn't to have its ears or tail pulled, or be ridden like a pony. Senior dogs may seem placid, but they may also have a short fuse with young children as well as young dogs. As your senior dog's mental health and physical health are interlinked, providing a stress-free environment for your senior is important.

Although senior dogs often do best in smaller households with just one or two adults and no competing pets or children, others thrive in a family environment and with the company of other dogs, especially if that is what

*Photo Courtesy of
Mary Ann Coffin*

they have always been used to. So, the rescue organization will do their best to match you up with a dog that suits your lifestyle. If fact, in the USA, the ASPCA has pioneered a campaign called "Adoption Ambassadors," where volunteers act as talent agents for their foster pets to find the best possible fit. But in the unlikely event that it doesn't work out, even after giving the dog plenty of time and patience to settle in, your dog should not be rehomed by you, but returned to the rescue under terms of the adoption agreement. This gives him the best chance of finding his forever home next time.

CHAPTER 3
Aging

Age is only a number; it's not a disease. But with aging, certain aspects of a dog's body will degenerate, making him more susceptible to ailments or diseases. Providing your dog with diligent care in his senior years will help slow down the aging process and keep him healthier for longer. In Chapter 4, there are many tips on how to look after your senior dog on a day to day basis. In this chapter, the aging process is explained so that you can understand what is happening to your dog's aging body and why it needs extra care to keep it healthy.

Photo Courtesy of
Lynzie Bacchus

Senses

Undoubtedly, dogs rely on their senses (hearing, vision, taste, touch, and especially smell) to give themselves plenty of information about their surroundings. But gradually with age, the senses can become less sharp.

Senses provide information, which is converted into nerve signals to the brain, where it is processed. Before a nerve signal is transmitted, the sense has to be greater than a certain threshold. For example, a sound has to be a certain volume or frequency, or a touch has to be a certain pressure. Age can lead to a deterioration in any of the senses, but in dogs, hearing and vision are most affected.

Photo Courtesy of Ashley Marks

When light enters the eye, it passes through the outer surface (cornea), through the lens (which focuses the light on the back of the eye) and hits the retina. As they age, the structures in the eye change. The fibers in the lens condense, leading to a cloudiness known as nuclear sclerosis. Nuclear sclerosis is not completely opaque, like cataracts which can also develop in old age. Some light can reach the back of the eye and your dog will still be able to see to some degree. An ophthalmological examination will be able to differentiate between cataracts and nuclear sclerosis.

HELPFUL TIP
Halo Vests

Blindness doesn't have to mean the end of mobility for your senior dog. One innovation for blind dogs is a halo vest. The halo vest consists of a vest fitted with a metal bumper that extends around your dog's face like a halo. This bumper alerts your dog when he is about to bump into something and can help restore confidence in dogs who are affected by blindness.

Photo Courtesy of
Sarah Vatcher

When the light hits the retina at the back of the eye, age related degeneration of this structure can also lead to altered vision. The retina is a sheet of photoreceptors, known as rods and cones. Rods provide vision in low light, and cones in bright light. Dogs have fewer cones in their retina than humans but more rods, so they enjoy excellent night vision in their younger days, but a lesser experience of color. Degeneration of the rods or cones can lead to night blindness or blindness in bright light, before finally, generalized blindness.

Age-related hearing loss is a common occurrence in most elderly dogs. Some people believe their dog is just ignoring them, but the reality is that he probably just can no longer hear certain frequencies or volumes. Various ailments and diseases can lead to hearing loss, such as tumors, ear infections and trauma, so it's important to differentiate age related hearing loss from more serious causes with your veterinarian.

Hearing loss in old age is not usually because of structural degeneration of the ear anatomy though. It usually is caused by geriatric degeneration of the nerves travelling from the ear to the brain. Unfortunately, age related hearing loss has no known cure. It's always a good idea to teach your dog hand signals alongside his verbal commands, in preparation for the possibility he will lose his hearing in his old age.

Musculoskeletal System

The musculoskeletal system is the part of the body which allows your dog to move. It's made up of muscles, joints, and bones, and with age, it can change. Changes in this system may adversely affect your dog's ability to exercise, and if you have a dog which has been trained for work or sport, these changes may make it necessary for your dog to retire from these particular activities.

A common ailment in joints, which becomes more common with age, is arthritis. Arthritis is a disease caused by normal forces on a previously injured joint, or abnormal forces (e.g. excessive weight) on a normal joint.

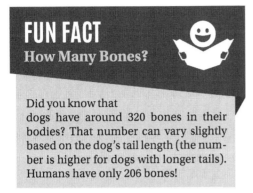

FUN FACT
How Many Bones?

Did you know that dogs have around 320 bones in their bodies? That number can vary slightly based on the dog's tail length (the number is higher for dogs with longer tails). Humans have only 206 bones!

Most dogs will eventually develop arthritis due to one of these reasons. Arthritis causes joints to become sore and reduces the range of flexion and extension. The disease process and treatment options are further discussed in Chapter 6. Diligent joint care throughout your dog's life can help slow the degeneration of his joints. Feeding a quality diet and joint supplements, ensuring your dog is fit, slim, and not excessively exercising will also help. Further information on these is discussed in Chapters 4 and 5.

With age, the prevalence of spinal disorders in dogs also increases, the most common of which is spondylosis deformans. This is when extra bone growth, known as a"spur", is laid down underneath the vertebrae. Spurs can be very painful and may lead to nerves becoming impinged, causing the hindquarters to weaken. The condition can happen in response to injury, but it is usually simply an age-related change to the spine.

Due to a decrease in mobility, older dogs, especially larger ones, tend to sleep and lie down more. The extra pressure on their elbow areas can form thickened areas of skin known as calluses. It's very common to see calluses on older dogs. They are usually not painful, but can bleed if severe.

In humans, bones usually decrease in density with age, but this is not common in dogs. However, inside the long bones, bone marrow can be found. With age, the bone marrow gradually becomes replaced with fat. Although bone marrow is not a component which contributes to strength, age-related changes can still have profound effects on the body. The bone marrow is responsible for making red blood cells, which carry oxygen around the body, and white blood cells which fight disease. Therefore, as the bone marrow deteriorates, it can cause anemia and reduced immunity.

Photo Courtesy of Teresa Umbelino

Digestion and Metabolism

With age, the efficiency of the digestive system lags, which is one reason why a senior dog's diet is so important. Diets are further discussed in Chapter 5. When the food moves through the intestine, it's pushed by muscular contractions causing a wave-like motion. This is called peristalsis. Peristalsis slows down with old age and can result in food remaining in the colon for longer. The colon is part of the large intestine which absorbs water, so the longer the food waste stays in there, the drier it becomes. This results in constipation. Unfortunately, it's common for this to be exacerbated by spondylosis deformans, with the resulting hindquarter weakness causing difficulty squatting to defecate, as well as firm stools.

Older dogs are prone to more health problems, most of which will require medication. Some medications have side effects that speed up or slow down peristalsis, and potentially cause nausea or diarrhea. Antibiotics can also cause the depletion of natural gut probiotics, known as flora, and this often leads to an overgrowth of opportunistic bacteria that create large amounts of gas. The gas in turn can cause bloating and flatulence.

Senior dogs also have a slower metabolism than younger dogs, and coupled with inactivity, this can easily lead to obesity. Obesity can cause a vicious cycle, if your dog is obese he will want to exercise less, and this will cause greater stress on his joints and heart, leading to a downwards spiral. An appropriate senior dog food diet will address the metabolism change to prevent this from happening.

Photo Courtesy of
Hailey Sobania

The liver also plays a large role in the digestive system, as it produces bile which helps to digest fats, and it metabolizes waste products. The liver only needs 20% function to survive. Age, drugs, toxins, and liver diseases can cause liver cirrhosis, which is a chronic, slow degeneration of the liver, where liver tissue is replaced by fibrous scar tissue. Even though the liver can cope with less function initially, if it is put under stress by medications, toxins, or anesthetics, these can easily cause liver failure. Symptoms and treatment of liver failure are discussed further in Chapter 6.

Mind

*Photo Courtesy of
Amanda BourQuard*

The brain is a complex anatomical structure. It controls how the body works as well as emotions, thoughts, and behavior. It's made up of several parts; the three most important of which are the cerebrum, the cerebellum, and the brainstem.

As the brain ages, it gradually becomes damaged. Scientists today believe that most of that damage is due to the effect of free radicals on the brain cells. Most free radicals cannot be avoided and are produced by the body, but free radicals can also be picked up from the environment.

Free radicals affect many different organs in the body, but the brain is particularly susceptible for several reasons. First, the brain has a high lipid content which free radicals like to target. It also has poor regeneration capabilities and limited defenses against free radicals. Finally, the brain has a high demand for oxygen, which is what free radicals are; unstable oxygen molecules.

The free radicals produced in the body come from mitochondria. A mitochondrion is the part of the cell which produces energy, but as a by-product, free radicals are also formed. Older mitochondria are less efficient at producing energy and produce more toxic free radicals than younger ones, so naturally, an older dog has more damaging free radicals in his blood circulation. The damage caused

HELPFUL TIP
Puzzles for Senior Dogs

While senior dogs may start slowing down in body, it's important to help them keep their mental faculties sharp. Puzzle toys are a great way to accomplish this. You might consider purchasing puzzle toys that require your dog to do some problem-solving in order to get a treat!

Photo Courtesy of
Miranda Schmitter

by the free radicals leads to decreased cognitive ability and can cause changes in behavior, such as decreased interaction, confusion, soiling the house, sleeping more, wandering aimlessly, and staring into space.

Senior dog nutrition plays a vital role in preventing free radical damage in the brain, as certain antioxidants, vitamins, and minerals can counteract this.

Excretions

Aging can have an effect on the ability of your dog to control his bladder and bowels. He may not find it as undignified as you might, but loss of control can lead to secondary skin issues from soiling and urine scald, as

Photo Courtesy of
Ashley Hall

40

Photo Courtesy of
Dondra Blackwell

well as a decrease in quality of life due to repeatedly having accidents around the house.

Loss of bowel control is usually secondary to development of lumbosacral spondylosis deformans in the spine. The nerves which travel from this section of the spine to the anus, which control the tone of the muscular sphincter holding it closed, can become damaged. As a result, the anus becomes flaccid and does not hold the stool inside well.

Loss of bladder control can also be due to nerve damage, resulting in the urethral sphincter losing tone. But more commonly, the urethral sphincter loses tone in old, spayed females, due to a lifetime of lacking estrogen. Estrogen is a hormone, produced by the reproductive system, that improves tone, and therefore helps the urinary sphincter to stay tightly shut. Urinary incontinence can be improved if the cause is due to a lack of estrogen, but if there is nerve damage, this is harder to manage.

***

Aging is an inevitable part of life, and if you've been blessed with a geriatric dog, it is in both your and his best interests to be diligent with his care. Even though certain parts of the body can degenerate over time and your dog will be more susceptible to certain diseases, age is not a disease itself. It is definitely possible to have an extremely healthy senior dog if he is provided with senior-specific care, which this book will help you with over the following chapters.

Photo Courtesy of
Mina Timmons

CHAPTER 4
Caring for a Senior Dog

As your dog reaches his senior years, his general care may need to be adjusted to cater for his growing needs. Most of these adjustments will be gradual changes which can be put in place around the house, and alterations to his general routine, over several months or even years. However, it is also beneficial to your senior to have increased veterinary care to pick up on any ailments early. As a result, if something is detected, there may need to be an immediate alteration to his lifestyle to ensure he has the best possible prognosis for the future. In this chapter, these alterations to his lifestyle will be discussed so that you can start making any necessary gradual changes to your dog's daily routine.

Photo Courtesy of Pat Meehan

Senior Veterinary Check-Ups

To ensure your senior dog is kept in top health, senior check-ups with your vet are recommended. This is in addition to your dog's usual annual vaccination visit. The reason for these checks is to ensure anything which is deteriorating is picked up very early in the course of the disease. That way it can be treated as soon as possible and the progression slowed.

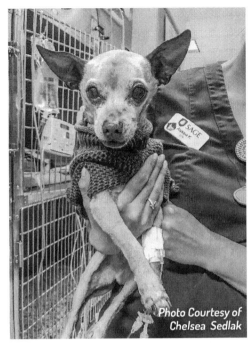

Photo Courtesy of Chelsea Sedlak

A senior wellness check will start with a physical exam. Your vet will check the head area first, the teeth for any excessive tartar, and the eyes for any cloudiness. Next, he will listen to the heart and lungs to make sure the heart is beating in a regular rhythm and the lungs are clear and not wheezing. Finally, he will feel the abdomen for any lumps as well as to check the size of the liver. He might try to feel the kidneys, but in larger dogs, they can be extremely hard to feel unless the dog is very thin.

Photo Courtesy of Amy Junes

After the clinical exam, your vet will probably take some blood to check for general organ health. The blood is usually taken from the jugular vein in the neck; however, some vets prefer the cephalic vein in the front leg. A small patch of hair will be clipped so the vet can see the vein and make the procedure as quick as possible for your dog. This blood test will give a good indication of the internal health of your dog and pick up on any very early-stage problems. These test results might be analyzed in conjunction with urinalysis results too. Urine is easy and cheap to test and gives

FUN FACT
First Veterinary School

Did you know that the profession of modern veterinary medicine is said to have begun in 1761 when Claude Bourgelat founded the Royal Veterinary School in Lyon, France? The Royal Veterinary School was founded in order to improve education for livestock management following a cattle plague in France. Bourgelat is considered a pioneer of modern veterinary medicine.

a wealth of information about your dog's kidneys, bladder, and endocrine system.

Finally, your vet may also perform a blood pressure test. This is much like a blood pressure test in a human, where a cuff is placed around the front leg and inflated. Older dogs may be prone to higher blood pressure due to kidney or heart disease, and therefore early detection will enable your dog to receive medication as necessary.

Routine Preventative Treatments

Vaccinations

Without a doubt, vaccinations are life-saving and have contributed to the reduction of some major canine diseases around the world. When your dog was young, you probably had him vaccinated against deadly diseases such as distemper, parvovirus, and hepatitis, as well as possibly leptospirosis, rabies, coronavirus, and parainfluenza. These vaccines usually require annual boosters to keep your dog's immunity up to date.

When dogs grow old, it's common for owners to start to question whether vaccinations are still necessary. There are several schools of thought on the matter, and unfortunately there is no absolute answer. However, by discussing matters with your vet, you should be able to formulate a routine preventative disease control plan which is appropriate for your dog.

Photo Courtesy of Samantha Sivils

Many veterinarians promote annual re-vaccination to ensure that the immune system is ready to fight off any infection that it comes into contact with. This is particularly important in older dogs whose immunity is not as effective as it once was. However, if you have vaccinated your dog every year for his whole life, there is research to suggest the residual immunity in your older dog will last for several years at a time. Therefore, some veterinarians feel that vaccinating senior dogs yearly is not worth the risk of potential vaccine reactions. If you wish to skip a yearly vaccination, it's advisable to perform a blood test to check the immunity levels of your dog, so you are not leaving him unprotected.

Regardless of which approach you and your veterinarian take for your senior, there are several things all veterinarians agree on. If you are in a rabies endemic area, a rabies vaccine should be administered yearly. In some areas, yearly vaccination is legally required. That said, many veterinarians agree that it is only necessary to vaccinate your dog against diseases to which he is susceptible. For example, if you don't live in an area where there is leptospirosis, then this vaccine is likely to be unnecessary.

It is worth bearing in mind, if you use kennels when you go on vacation, that your dog will probably need to have an up-to-date vaccination record, at least for certain diseases. So before letting the annual boosters lapse, check the requirements with your regular boarding kennel.

Parasite Control

Parasites such as worms, fleas, and ticks are a threat to all dogs, regardless of their age. However, when your dog reaches his senior years, his natural ability to deal with parasites deteriorates, and the damage which occurs in his body from the infestation can be much more serious.

Routine parasite control should continue regularly, and care should be taken not to allow it to lapse. De-wormers against roundworms and tapeworms should be provided every 3 to 6 months depending on whether your dog likes to scavenge on his walks. Most de-wormers come in the form of tablets or treats; however, some de-worming products are mixed with flea and tick prevention in the form of spot-on pipettes. Flea and tick preventative treatments should also be given regularly at the dosing interval required for the product. Some flea and tick treatments last for a month, whereas others last for several months, and so providing your dog with continual care will provide him with the best opportunity to stay healthy.

Neutering and Spaying

It's a common belief that old dogs cannot be safely neutered or spayed, or that there are no benefits. However, if your senior dog is still healthy, spaying her or neutering him provides plenty of advantages. Older female dogs are prone to uterine infections, known as pyometra, which can be life-threatening. They can also develop ovarian or uterine cancers, and removing the reproductive organs eliminates this danger. Neutering male dogs also eliminates the chances of testicular cancers and decreases the risk of prostate disease. More than 60% of unneutered males have enlarged prostates, and this can lead to an inability to urinate and defecate, and can even turn cancerous. Neutering your male dog allows his prostate to return to its normal size.

Of course, all surgeries involve risk, and older dogs are considered higher risk. However, in the hands of a competent veterinarian, senior dogs can be very safely spayed and neutered. Before surgery, your veterinarian should run a blood test to ensure your dog is healthy. This blood test ensures the liver and kidneys are working efficiently so that the anesthetic can be metabolized and filtered out of the body effectively. Your veterinarian

Photo Courtesy of
Jillian Cutone

Photo Courtesy of
Jessica Powers

will also check your dog's heart to ensure it can withstand the anesthetic, as gaseous anesthetic can cause blood pressure to drop. If your vet is concerned, he may decide to give your dog intravenous fluid therapy to keep the pressure normal and speed up his recovery.

Your veterinarian is the best person to discuss spaying, neutering and preventative health care with, as he will be able to help you make the most informed decisions to ensure your dog has the healthiest life possible throughout his senior years.

Around the House

An overview of senior dogs in the house has already been covered in Chapter 1, but it is worth looking at some aspects in greater detail, as you adapt your dog's care for later in life.

Bedding

Probably the single most significant thing you can do for your older dog is invest in a high-quality orthopedic bed to cushion his painful joints throughout his senior years. There are several reasons for this.

Photo Courtesy of
Heather Voelker

Firstly, as your dog becomes arthritic, the effect of his body weight on his bony protuberances will aggravate his pain, and this will be evident when he gets up. A senior dog's skin is also thinner and more sensitive, making it more prone to pressure sores. An orthopedic bed, which is often cushioned with memory foam, distributes your dog's body weight evenly so that his joints are not under pressure when he is resting. It also allows for greater positive alignment of the spine and limbs so your dog is not resting in an unnatural position that could put a strain on his body.

Secondly, your dog will appreciate the warmth and comfort of an orthopedic bed, rather than feeling the floor or a hard base through a thin bed. Older dogs are more sensitive to cold temperatures, which can aggravate their stiffness, so a plusher textile and cushioned base helps them maintain their body temperature at rest.

Thirdly, investing in a comfortable bed gives your dog a place of safety that increases his sense of emotional wellbeing, and alleviates anxiety, to which older dogs can be susceptible.

For dogs that have always slept on the couch or their owner's bed, tempting your senior dog to use his own bed as a matter of his preference, could be helpful if your dog develops incontinence. This is because his bed will be much easier to clean than your furniture. Female dogs that have been spayed early in life are especially prone to leakage at night. This is due to the lack of estrogen throughout their lives, causing laxity in their later years. Ideally, you should look for a bed with removable covers that can be thrown in the washing machine. Otherwise, some smaller beds can be machine washed, or larger ones may be washed by hand if they become soiled.

You can line your dog's bed with a deep pile material known as "Vet Bedding," which is usually sold by length from a roll. Dogs love the comfort of vet bedding, and it's easy to wash, so is ideal for an elderly dog.

The final thing to consider is where to situate your dog's bed. If you have had your dog all his life, he no doubt already has his favorite spots, so just be certain that where you place his bed is not in a drafty or high traffic area. Most dogs prefer to be near their humans, so they may appreciate their bed to be in the living room, although if you spend a lot of time in the kitchen or office, your older dog may need an additional bed in those places too. Other dogs may like to be near the door to keep watch, but they mustn't be in a constant draft in their senior years, so make sure you block any drafts by the door if that happens to be your senior's favored spot.

Stairs

If you live in a house that has more than one floor, and your dog has always been allowed upstairs, you may notice him struggling more with the stairs as he advances into his senior years. This may be due to arthritis or joint disease, or weakness in his hind end due to medication or neurological issues.

Sometimes, these physical issues can be improved. Talk to your vet to see if your dog needs a change in his medication or would benefit from

Photo Courtesy of
Jada Blankenship

physiotherapy or hydrotherapy to strengthen his hind end, or acupuncture to relieve his discomfort and stiffness.

Wooden stairs can be especially slippery for dogs as they need to power off from their back legs. One modification you could consider would be to fit a carpet runner or non-slip treads to give your elderly dog better traction. This will also improve his confidence going back down the stairs, especially if he has balance issues.

If your dog has always slept upstairs, it is natural for him to continue to want to go there. So, if he voluntarily starts sleeping downstairs because he finds the stairs too difficult, it is an indicator that his pain is becoming significant. Also, for some dogs with worsening conditions such as hip or elbow dysplasia or patella luxation, using the stairs may cause injury. So, if your elderly dog chooses or can be encouraged to sleep downstairs, this will be to his benefit.

If the vet has told you your dog should not be using the stairs, you may consider fitting a stair gate at the bottom of the stairs. If your dog is small enough to be picked up, you may then still be able to carry him upstairs for the night, but you should also fit a gate at the top of the stairs to prevent him from going back down on his own.

Separation anxiety may become an issue for older dogs that still want to sleep upstairs with their humans, but find their way blocked by the stair gate. If your dog cannot settle on his own downstairs but is too large to carry, you may be able to assist him up the stairs with a mobility harness that fits under his tummy. This process should never be rushed, and the downward journey in the morning should also be assisted, even though your dog may seem to find it easier.

For other situations where your dog used to jump in his younger years, such as on and off furniture, and up and down the yard steps, consider the use of a dog ramp. These should have a grippy surface, but you should still supervise, to ensure your dog doesn't jump or fall off the edge. You shouldn't expect your dog to know instinctively how to use a ramp. If he has never done agility sports, he will need to be taught with guidance and treats. And you should always be sure the ramp is stable so he doesn't lose his confidence once he gains it.

Smoke Exposure

If your dog has grown up in an indoor environment exposed to cigarette smoke, studies suggest he may experience some detrimental effects on his

Photo Courtesy of Emily Johnsen

health by the time he gets to his senior years. These include eye infections, skin conditions, respiratory diseases, and even nasal or lung cancer.

It can be upsetting to realize that your dog has suffered the effects of passive smoking over the years and the damage may have already been done. However, it is never too late to help your dog during his senior years by only smoking outside the house, and washing your hands after smoking, as well as regularly cleaning any textiles that have been in contact with cigarette smoke. It is also important to keep ashtrays, cigarette butts, vaping products, and nicotine replacement products well out of reach of your dog.

Environmental Enrichment

As dogs age, they are prone to cognitive decline just like us. And also, just as with humans, it has been proven that providing the right kind of mental stimulation can improve cognition. But since you can't teach your dog to play Sudoku, what can you do to keep his brain ticking during his senior years?

Toys aren't just for puppies! Your senior dog may have always enjoyed playing with you as well as on his own, and this continues to fulfill a vital role in his old age. Interacting with his human is especially valuable, although the games you play together should now take into account your dog's physical frailties. For example, playing with a tug rope should not be as vigorous now your dog's teeth are getting loose, and fetch should not be as energetic, as sharp stops and tight turns can damage your dog's back. Your dog may also enjoy comfort toys, which can help his mental wellbeing during this phase of life. Other than toys, continuing to train your dog in later life helps his brain to remain active.

As well as cognitive decline, many dogs experience a gradual loss of vision as they get older. This may be due to cataracts, which can eventually

Photo Courtesy of
Becky Groseth

*Photo Courtesy of
Kelly Collins*

cause blindness. Cataracts are not to be confused with nuclear sclerosis, which is the natural clouding of the lens seen in most elderly dogs, which doesn't affect eyesight to a significant degree. Cataracts can just be part of the aging process, or they can develop from trauma to the eye that occurred earlier in life. It is sometimes possible to treat cataracts and other conditions affecting your dog's vision, as discussed in Chapter 6.

For senior dogs that are experiencing vision loss, it is beneficial to keep the home environment consistent. So that means no rearranging the furniture or major home improvements if possible, during these few short years. Some modifications can be made for a blind or partially sighted dog. These include keeping the floor area free of obstructions and adding padding to hard objects such as table legs. Your dog is still guided by his sense of smell and has a route map of the scents in your house, so it is important not to interfere with this too much. Textures can also help, such as a mat at a doorway that your dog can sense under his paws.

Your dog's environment may become more home-focused as he advances in years, so providing him with enrichment makes sure he maintains the best quality of life for as long as possible.

Exercise

Exercise was discussed in Chapter 1, and it continues to be the number one protector against cognitive decline and sustainer of physical fitness. However, you may still be wondering just how much exercise your senior dog needs per day.

How Much for My Dog?

Every breed comes with a guideline for the amount of exercise it needs during the adult years. This is greater than what your dog needed as a puppy when his bones were still developing, and also greater than he needs now as a senior dog. As seniors are prone to weight gain due to the slow-down in their metabolism, it is important that they still get out and about daily, even if it is less than before.

Photo Courtesy of Alexa Patterson

When assessing how much exercise your senior dog needs, you need to be guided by what you see. For example, let's take the breed average of one hour of exercise a day for an adult Cocker Spaniel. As your dog ages, you may notice him slowing down on his walks. He may struggle and tire, or he may be very stiff the next day. This is an indicator that you need to reduce the duration or intensity of his walks. You may drop the duration to three-quarters, then half an hour. Or even better, you may split his walk into two or three shorter walks. Little and often is best for stiff joints.

Photo Courtesy of Deineira Smith

On the other hand, if your dog is starting to look a little portly in his old age, but can still keep up the pace, maintaining his regular exercise routine will help ward off the effects of his lower metabolic rate. That said, you may also need to adjust his diet.

Older dogs generally appreciate walks that they know well, especially if they are losing their sight. For visually impaired dogs, getting out is especially stimulating, as dogs see with their noses, and there is always a wealth of scents to explore in the outside world.

You should go at your dog's pace, allowing him to use his senses, and if the weather is cold or wet, he will benefit from a coat to stay warm, or just a day playing games with you indoors.

Types of Exercise

Walking is not the only form of exercise suitable for your senior dog. Many dogs enjoy swimming, which is excellent, as it doesn't put stress on the joints. However, you shouldn't let your senior swim in fast currents that he no longer has the strength for, or stay in the water long enough to get cold. A drying robe is a good investment for dogs that like to swim. Otherwise, hydrotherapy pools provide a safe swimming environment, and your dog can be dried off quickly after the session.

For dogs that have led active lives, such as working dogs, and those that have participated in sports like agility, there may be a reluctance to slow down. As active dogs are generally very fit, the effects of old age may not be apparent until quite late in life. Even after working dogs are no longer being sent out to flush or retrieve, they will still enjoy being out in the countryside or watching the hunt from the van.

HELPFUL TIP
Treadmill Time

While there are many options for outdoor exercise for your dog, indoor exercise can require a bit of creativity. If you have a treadmill, this dilemma may have just gotten a little easier! Smaller breeds of dog may be able to utilize a regular human treadmill. To determine if your treadmill is an appropriate length for your dog, make sure that the belt surface of your treadmill is 2 to 2.5 times the length of your dog. If you choose to exercise your dog on a treadmill it's important to observe all the recommended safety precautions, including (but not limited to) not leashing your dog to the treadmill, not allowing your dog to go faster than a trot, using caution when feeding treats (some dogs cannot walk and eat simultaneously), and consulting with your veterinarian to ensure that your dog is healthy enough for this activity.

For dogs trained in agility, there is still a course for seniors, where the jumps are lower, the weaves wider, and the obstacles are set up to minimize the impact on older joints. Other forms of exercise suitable for senior dogs include obedience, nose work, and "freestyle," which is low-impact dancing with owner and dog.

Car Ramps

For most people, continuing to take their dog out and about involves using the car, and where an adult dog will leap inside, when he gets to his senior years, jumping in and out of the car is more of an effort and even physically harmful.

Car ramps are widely available these days and well worth the investment, both for your dog and for your own back if he is heavy to lift. Some are wooden, but most are lightweight plastic and hinge in the middle to fold up for storage in your vehicle.

Photo Courtesy of
Will VanHuss

If you are not already using ramps around your home, you will have to show your dog how to use it at first. Simply guiding him up and down the ramp initially should show him that it's less painful than trying to jump. But if he is scared, encouraging him with treats and praise will soon demonstrate that even old dogs can learn new tricks!

Grooming

All dogs, whether short, medium or long-haired, require regular grooming throughout their lives. You may have had your dog professionally groomed over the years, which means he will be well used to a salon environment for his continuing senior care. But regardless of whether your dog has professional grooming sessions, there are certain aspects of basic grooming care that you need to attend to on a more frequent basis. And as your dog enters his later years, there are additional considerations to ensure your dog is comfortable with being groomed and gets the full benefit from it.

Coat Care

If your senior dog is a short-haired breed, you will have enjoyed the benefit of his low-maintenance coat throughout his life, and he may not have been brushed regularly. But in his later years, it is important that he learns to accept and even enjoy being brushed regularly, as an older dog's skin can be more prone to dead skin and yeast infections, and brushing helps to stimulate circulation in the skin, keeping it healthy.

Most senior dogs, especially those with short coats, will appreciate softer brushes at this time of life, as their skin is thinner and more sensitive than it once was.

If you own a dog with a longer coat, he should be well-used to being brushed, as this has always been important to remove mats and loose hair. However, senior dogs can become grumpy in their old age and less tolerant. They may not be as compliant when the brush comes out as they were in their younger years. It is important to remember that your older dog's joints and muscles may be sore, and he may not be comfortable standing in one position for any length of time. So, you should keep your grooming sessions short and sweet. It is useful to always have the brush close at hand, so you can gently brush your dog while he is lying down, and then later when he lies on the other side, you can groom him again. If you have to manually turn your dog, keep it slow and gentle. Regularly petting and massaging your older dog will alert you to any mats that may need teasing or cutting out, as well as any lumps or bumps that your vet may need to look at.

Some breeds, such as Collies, have a thick undercoat to protect them from extreme weather conditions, and as this layer is functional, it is not usual to clip these breeds short. But for some long or medium-haired breeds, a full body clip can reduce the discomfort of grooming out mats and allow more air to reach the skin. Whether or not you clip your dog, some areas need particular attention. For older dogs who cannot bend to clean themselves as effectively, you may consider a sanitary cut or hygiene clip around their rear end. For

Photo Courtesy of Maureen Simpson

dogs with a lot of facial hair, you should trim their bangs and muzzle near their eyes with blunt-ended scissors, so they can still see, and dogs with hairy feet should have the sides and bottom of their paws gently clipped, to improve traction. You should also check between the toes for seeds like foxtails, that can work their way in and cause infection.

Nail Care

When grooming and checking the feet, you should also keep an eye on the length of your senior dog's nails; if these get too long it will affect his traction, and eventually could cause him pain by pushing up his toes or even curling into them.

Dogs that are regularly walked on hard surfaces will wear their nails down naturally, but if your elderly dog doesn't get out quite as much these

Photo Courtesy of Jane Herron

days, his nails could start to grow faster than they are being worn down, and they will need to be clipped.

If your dog goes to the groomer regularly, his nails will always be kept short, and this is ideal, as it means the sensitive inner part known as the quick, will not become too long. The quick is often visible through the transparent outer part of a white nail, but with a black nail, judging where it starts is more of a challenge. You can sometimes spot the quick by looking at the underside of the nail, where the keratinous outer layer forms a seam.

If nails are neglected, the quick can grow long and may be more easily nicked when the nails are cut. This can result in

HELPFUL TIP
Oh No! A Broken Nail!

If you notice your dog limping following a yelp of pain, he may have a broken nail. The first step in addressing a broken nail is to restrain your dog or have a partner do so. Your dog may try to pull away from you while you're examining his paw, causing more damage. Thus, restraining him is an important first step. Next, you'll want to control the bleeding. Once these steps have been accomplished, call your veterinarian for additional instructions. It's important to address broken nails in order to prevent infection and manage your dog's pain. Broken nails can be an inevitable part of senior pet ownership, but keeping your dog's nails trimmed is an excellent method for prevention.

profuse bleeding that can be alarming. If you are clipping your dog's nails and catch the quick, your dog is sure to react, which can damage his confidence for future sessions. So, if you can't see the quick, you should just clip off small parts of the nail at a time until you see a whitish-grey circle. Or you can use a battery-operated nail grinder, which many owners and dogs prefer.

If your dog's nail is bleeding, don't panic, or you will transfer your stress to the dog. If you have styptic powder, apply this with a moistened Q-tip and apply pressure for at least 30 seconds. Or if you do not have styptic powder, you can improvise with corn starch, flour, baking soda or soap. Whatever you use, compression is important to allow the blood to coagulate, which can take a few minutes. If the nail is still bleeding after 20 minutes, you may need a vet.

If your dog is anxious about having his nails clipped, especially if he has had a bad experience, you can help him make a positive association with the clippers by always bringing out an especially irresistible treat, such as tiny pieces of sausage, so that he learns the ordeal is not so bad.

Ear Care

Older dogs can be especially prone to yeast or bacterial infections in their ear canal, especially floppy-eared breeds like Spaniels, as the ear flap prevents ventilation. Also, for dogs that love to swim, dirty water can lead to infection.

You will know your dog has a problem if he is scratching his ear, shaking his head, or if you notice a foul odor from his ear. When it gets to this stage, a visit to the vet is called for. However, there are certain things you can do to prevent your older dog from having problems with his ears.

During your regular grooming sessions, you should always have a good look at your dog's ears for any signs of irritation, like inflammation, or evidence he has been scratching. You should also look for any foreign bodies, such as grass seeds at the entrance to his ear canal, and have a good sniff to familiarize yourself with what is normal. You should then use a canine ear cleaning solution and apply it to each ear in turn, holding your dog's ear closed for a few seconds, then allowing him to shake his head. This will lift any debris and bring it to the surface. You can then wipe out the ear canal and surrounding area.

You may also use blunt-ended scissors to trim any mats or excess hair from under the ear and the ear flap, as well as any hair protruding from the ear canal. This helps airflow, making the ear environment less favorable to microorganisms. Ear plucking remains a controversial practice, even amongst professional groomers, as it can be uncomfortable and may even introduce infection. So trimming is the safest approach for your more sensitive senior.

Bathing

Older dogs still need bathing, even if they are not being regularly hosed down after muddy walks like they were in their younger years.

Your senior dog's skin is drier and thinner than it was, and he may be suffering from skin conditions. Now more than ever, he requires a shampoo formulation that is appropriate for his needs. For most seniors, this is simply a mild, non-drying dog shampoo. The addition of oatmeal is excellent for senior skin. But if your dog has a skin condition such as fungal infection, you should obtain a prescription shampoo from your vet, and use it as directed.

Cold water is no longer suitable to bathe your senior dog, even if he will happily swim in a lake or the ocean. When you bathe him, he is standing still, is probably tense, and is sensitive to the cold. If you are bathing him in a bathtub, you should place a rubber mat in the bottom to prevent your dog from slipping and fill it with lukewarm water, before gently lifting your dog in. Otherwise, you can bathe your dog in the shower, but always test the spray temperature and make sure it is running consistently before turning it on your dog.

After wetting your dog's coat, massage the shampoo in gently. If it is a therapeutic shampoo, it may need to be left for a few minutes before being rinsed off thoroughly. If you have a full bathtub, it is less messy to let the water run out and towel your dog off in the tub, before lifting him out carefully. He may then enjoy a further rub with the towel and a massage, even if the bath itself has been torture!

Make sure you thoroughly dry your old dog after his bath, especially before allowing him back outside. Drying coats made from towels are widely available and can make sure your senior dog doesn't catch a chill.

Keeping your dog clean and well-groomed in his senior years not only means he looks his best but ensures his everyday health needs are addressed at the same time.

Dental Care

Dental disease is a common problem in senior pets with the majority of dogs having some degree of dental disease. Diligent dental care will help preserve your senior's oral health as long as possible. This is important, as when your senior dog cannot eat comfortably, he will not receive the appropriate nutrients to stay healthy.

Photo Courtesy of
Yvonne Maddocks

Preventative Dental Care

The adult dog's mouth has 42 teeth which cannot be replaced if they fall out or become damaged. Therefore, preventative dental care will help to pre-

*Photo Courtesy of
Sherry Schuessler*

serve them for as long as possible. When bacteria and food build up on the base of the teeth, plaque forms and the teeth become weakened. Removing the plaque regularly will help to keep the teeth strong. This can be done through regular examinations of the mouth, tooth brushing, and dental chews.

The best way to examine your dog's teeth is on a day he's feeling happy and relaxed. If he feels nervous or in a bad mood, you might make things worse by examining things. You can ask your veterinarian to check your dog's mouth whenever you are there for a check-up, however checking the mouth yourself every few weeks will help pick up problems early.

Start by lifting the front lips and looking at the incisors. They should be white or cream with minimal tartar. They should not be wobbly, and the gums should not be receding. The next teeth to look at are the canines. These build up a lot of tartar easily. Finally pull the cheeks right back to view the pre-molars and molars. It's a common mistake not to pull the cheeks back far enough to view the very back teeth, so be aware of this.

If you see a tooth that is grey and much darker than the rest, it is a sign that it is dying from the inside pulp area, and even if it is not wobbly or covered in tartar, your veterinarian should assess the tooth.

Regular brushing will prevent tooth decay, gingivitis and tartar build-up throughout your dog's life and especially in his senior years.

Always brush your dog's teeth with dog toothpaste, as human toothpaste often contains a sweetener called xylitol. This is extremely dangerous to your dog as it can cause his blood glucose to drastically drop. This, in turn, will cause seizures and could potentially even lead to death. Dog toothpaste contains many enzymes, which specifically dissolve off the tartar from the tooth. However, once the tartar has become extensive, it will not solve the problem, but it will stop it from worsening.

To have the most effect, tooth brushing should be performed from early on in your dog's life, but starting in his senior years is better than never. If your dog is not used to brushing, he may resent it at first, so try to make it fun with plenty of positive rewards afterward.

In addition to brushing, dental chews can also help to remove tartar. Dental chews work by causing a mild abrasion as they are bitten through. They either help remove tartar through sucking it off or cracking it off. There are many different size and shaped treats around. You should choose the appropriate size for your breed of dog, or it might not remove the tartar appropriately.

Dental chews should be given as part of your dog's daily diet, and not in addition to it. Therefore, if your dog needs 1000 calories per day and the treat is 150 calories, make sure you subtract that amount of food from the daily quantity recommended.

Some people like to use natural treats such as knucklebones or antlers to provide abrasion to the teeth to help clean them. However, older dogs may easily crack their teeth on these harder treats, or experience bleeding from the gums, so they should ideally be avoided.

Physical Therapy

Older dogs can benefit from physical therapy to help their aging body stay in the best condition possible. This should always be carried out by professionals, and your veterinarian will be able to provide you with referrals to canine physical therapists who are specialized in these fields.

Physiotherapy

The idea of physiotherapy for a dog seems a strange one for many people. But physiotherapists are not just for athletes and sporting injuries. Physiotherapy aims to restore the normal function of the physical body, which may be afflicted by disease, injury, or age. This is achieved through physical exercises, stretches, laser therapy, TENS therapy, and muscle manipulation. Dogs can't tell us where it hurts and many hide their discomfort until it is unbearable. A physiotherapist will be able to pick up on subtle discomforts throughout the body and provide rehabilitation exercises to suit your dog's needs.

The end goal of physiotherapy sessions for your dog is to regain a normal range of movement in all joints which may have had restricted or painful movement, reduce the impact of the underlying problem on the body, particularly where muscles are compensating for an underlying issue, and improve the healing process so that your dog can return to normal as quickly as possible. It is an excellent therapy for all older dogs to access, to make sure they are feeling young again.

Photo Courtesy of Val Allan

Not only will a veterinary physiotherapist aim to improve the comfort and function of your senior with hands-on therapy and exercises, but he will also advise you on adaptations that you can make to your dog's environment to help him go about his daily tasks in an easier way.

Massage

Massage is more than just rubbing your dog's muscles. When done properly, it improves blood flow to the muscles, which in turn releases tension and improves healing. So, if your dog is struggling with underlying joint problems, the aching muscles which are supporting the joints will benefit greatly from a daily massage.

Therapeutic massages are usually performed by veterinary physiotherapists, and it is advisable to initially have a professional treat your dog to ensure no harm is being done. But once you have been given the go ahead to massage your dog at home, it can easily be done every evening when he is quiet and sleepy. There are several massage strokes that you can apply to your dog and asking your canine physiotherapist to show you is the best way to learn. However, there are also excellent videos online of people demonstrating the techniques.

The first stroke to apply to your dog is called effleurage. This is a firm, slow stroke using the palm of your hand down the back and the legs. This helps to warm up the muscles and improve blood flow. After warming up the body with effleurage, a massage stroke called petrissage can be performed, which is similar to gently kneading the muscles. This helps relax the muscles and release tension. The massage can then be finished off with some gentle tapotement over the bigger areas of muscle, which are light, brisk percussive movements with the edge of your hands.

Hydrotherapy

Hydrotherapy is another therapy that is often performed by veterinary physiotherapists; however veterinary nurses and specifically trained hydrotherapists may also offer the service. Hydrotherapy is so much more than just swimming. It is highly therapeutic both for a dog's body and mind. For conditions that are exacerbated by weight, such as arthritis or degenerative changes in the spinal cord, hydrotherapy is an excellent way to build strength without putting stress on those areas.

A hydrotherapy pool is not a normal swimming pool. Generally, it is quite small and the water is heated. This in itself is soothing to uncomfortable muscles and joints. Pools have ramps for entry and exit, and your dog will swim with a harness to ensure he maintains a proper position when he is in the water. The hydrotherapist will be in the pool with your dog to ensure he swims in a beneficial manner for his ailments.

Photo Courtesy of Shianne May

Some pools have jets to provide resistance for your dog to swim against or an underwater treadmill to encourage a walking motion instead of a swimming motion.

In addition to helping build up the strength of your dog and slow down any degenerative conditions, hydrotherapy is also an excellent tool to help your dog build fitness and shed pounds. This, in turn, reduces pressure on aging joints. Older dogs frequently struggle to lose weight or maintain their fitness because of reduced mobility. This can trigger a downward spiral where reduced mobility causes weight gain, and weight gain reduces mobility. Hydrotherapy can help put a stop to that.

Acupuncture

Acupuncture is an ancient therapy, initially discovered by the Chinese, and while some veterinary acupuncture therapists still practice Chinese acupuncture, more practitioners now practice a Western version. It helps provide your senior dog with potent pain relief without the need for drugs.

The body is full of nerves that run around the body which connect the brain to the periphery, and in certain areas of the body, these nerves run together in thick bundles. The Chinese describe these nerve bundles as meridians, where there is a flow of energy. These are nerves sending electrical signals to the brain.

When a needle is placed into a region close to the nerve bundle, it causes a release of endorphins, which are natural chemical messengers. Endorphins cause the body to do many things, including relax, increase blood flow, slow heart rate, and induce a sleepy feeling. However, the most potent effect they have on the body is provide pain relief. Endorphins work on the cells of the body similarly to morphine.

The endorphins not only cause local pain relief where the needles are inserted, but they also travel up the nerve bundles to the spinal cord. They infiltrate a small area of the spinal cord, both up towards the head and down towards the body, and all the nerves which come off that segment also have the effects of the endorphins. Therefore, it is possible to achieve pain relief without direct needling of those areas. For example, the bladder can have great relief from acupuncturing points which cause an endorphin release in the lower spine.

Acupuncture is an excellent treatment modality for older dogs who are struggling with painful conditions. It is particularly useful for treating dogs who have underlying major organ disease, and cannot tolerate pain relief drugs without detrimental side effects. Veterinarians are the main providers of acupuncture, and in the UK, only veterinarians are allowed to practice acupuncture on animals. However, elsewhere around the world, veterinary nurses and physiotherapists also offer acupuncture. Regardless of who offers the acupuncture, it is worth enquiring about the type of training they have had and what type of acupuncture they offer.

***

There is not a definitive point in time when your dog crosses over the threshold from middle-aged to old, and therefore there is not a definitive point in time when you should put into practice all that has been discussed in this chapter. However, just as aging is a gradual process, it is worth slowly phasing in some of these things to help your dog transition into his senior years as smoothly and as healthily as possible. Your veterinarian is an excellent point of contact for advice about your senior and his ailments, and therefore when making any major changes to his lifestyle, consulting your veterinarian is always a wise idea.

CHAPTER 5
Nutrition

Feeding your dog the correct diet is essential for his wellbeing. At various life-stages, dogs need different balances of nutrients; protein, fats, carbohydrates, minerals and vitamins. Therefore, feeding your senior dog a puppy food is not going to be ideal for his health. The nutrients in his food all play their own individual roles. Proteins are the nutrient which helps build up muscles and repairs them if they become damaged. It's important that muscles stay strong in senior dogs to help support their aging bones and joints. Fats are an excellent energy source and help keep the skin, coat, and brain healthy. In senior dogs, it is common for cognitive ability to decline, and therefore, healthy fats can help maintain mental function. Carbohydrates are an excellent source of instant energy to help your dog stay active. Finally, vitamins and minerals are vital for nerves to send signals around the body, as well as cause muscles to contract. The optimum balance of these nutrients depends on your dog's life stage.

*Photo Courtesy of
Angela Zeigler*

Pet manufacturers invest a significant amount of time and money into formulating the perfect balance of nutrients in their recipes so that you don't have to. By purchasing a senior-specific dog food, you can be confident that your dog is receiving all the essential nutrients he needs. However, there are still many variations between brands of dog food, so it is important to do your research when choosing a new food. On average, around the age of 7 is a good time to consider transitioning your dog to a senior food.

Not only is food important for a senior dog, but the right health supplements can also help your dog stay healthy. Additional minerals and vitamins, omega oils, joint supplements, and probiotics are all available on the market for senior pets. Not all dogs will need supplements in their older age, and your veterinarian can assist in recommending ones which are most suitable for your dog as necessary. Helping your dog maintain an excellent diet early on in life, along with providing any necessary supplements, will help him stay healthier for far longer.

In this chapter, you will learn all about the most important aspects of senior nutrition to help you make the most informed choices for your dog's diet.

Senior Dog Food

Senior dog food is very different from puppy or adult dog food. While many senior dogs will do just fine on adult dog food if they are active, healthy, and a good weight, a senior dog food is more specific for the conditions and aging challenges they face in their later years.

One of the main differences between adult and senior dog food is the calorie content. Obesity in senior dogs is a common problem, and can have a major impact on their welfare. Obesity is common because of many reasons. Some older dogs have joint conditions which make

HELPFUL TIP

Recognizing a Mineral Deficiency

Your dog's nutritional needs and digestion will change as he ages. If you notice any significant changes in your dog's coat or skin, this may be a sign of a nutritional deficiency that needs to be fixed either by a change in diet or with supplements. A coat that is losing color, falling out in patches, or appears dull could be a sign of a copper deficiency, while a zinc deficiency presents with hair loss, skin cracking, or skin ulcers. If your dog starts eating dirt or feces, it can be a sign of mineral deficiency" right before the last sentence. Do not attempt to make a diagnosis without the help of a veterinarian as these symptoms can also be a sign of something more serious.

Photo Courtesy of
Tommy McInulty

them less mobile, whereas others simply have a slower metabolism. Excessive weight can put strain on arthritic joints as well as major organs, especially the heart. Therefore, most senior dog foods are relatively low in calories. In fact, a senior dog needs 20% less calories than he did in his middle-aged years to maintain the same weight. To ensure this doesn't lead to excessive hunger, senior dog foods are usually higher in fiber than other life-stages. This helps keep your dog full longer and also helps improve his gastrointestinal health.

Fiber is also great at stimulating the gut. Older dogs can easily develop constipation due to a slower gut, spinal abnormalities, and decreased mobility. Suitable fiber content for a senior dog food is between 3% and 5%.

Elderly dogs are also more prone to dental disease, where tartar builds up on the teeth, leading to decay and gum disease. Most dogs will need a dental procedure at some stage in their life, as discussed in Chapter 4. Diet can be extremely helpful in preventing further dental disease though. Many senior dog foods come in a dry form, so that as your dog bites through the kibble, the abrasion on the teeth helps remove tartar. Dry food alone will never clean the teeth enough to reverse dental disease, but if your dog has had a dental procedure, ensuring he has a dry senior diet will help him avoid having another one as he ages. The only time that dry food might not be appropriate is if your elderly dog has arthritis in his jaw joint, or the dental disease is very painful and underlying health conditions preclude him from being able to have a dental procedure. This usually only happens in very old age and can be helped by providing a soft food which is easier to chew through. However, this will not help the teeth, so following the steps laid out in Chapter 4 for dental care is imperative to help keep your older dog's teeth clean and comfortable.

If your senior dog has specific health problems, for example kidney disease or liver disease, which is common with old age, a health-specific diet might be more appropriate for him, compared to a senior diet. These diets are specifically formulated with lower levels of proteins and different mineral balances to prevent stress on the failing organs. Your veterinarian will be the best person to discuss these with, to ensure your dog has the most ideal nutrition for his condition.

If your dog doesn't have a health condition and you are transitioning him to a senior food, it's likely that when choosing a senior diet, you will be presented with many choices on the pet store shelves. Not all senior diets are the same, and it's easy to be led by persuasive marketing. However, there are some easy ways to determine which is the best diet for your dog.

First, look at the ingredients. The ingredients are listed in order of weight, and therefore, the ingredient with the highest quantity by weight will be the first ingredient on the list. Very high on the list should be meat-based proteins, such as turkey, beef, chicken, lamb, duck, or fish. Other good sources of proteins high on the list can include peas and eggs. It's important to remember that meat meal is dehydrated meat, and therefore very lightweight. As a result, it contributes 300% more protein than the equivalent of its fresh weight, and will be lower down the list in order of weight. Often the upper half of the list are filler ingredients, such as grains. These are useful carbohydrates, but they should not be making up the bulk of the ingredients. Grains should always be whole grains, such as brown rice, oatmeal, and barley. They should ideally not be white rice or maize, as these are empty calories and do not contribute many nutrients. Vegetables should also make up a large proportion of the ingredients. These provide fiber, minerals and vitamins. Vegetables such as carrots, sweet potato, pumpkin, potato, peas, and spinach are all popular additions to dog food. Fruits, such as blueberries and cranberries are also sometimes added, as

Photo Courtesy of
Kate Price

these provide plenty of anti-oxidants to help fight free radicals and improve the immune system.

Also, in addition to natural ingredients, senior dog food needs to be carefully balanced with refined ingredients. Therefore, it is common to see additional minerals and vitamins further down on the ingredient list. It's extremely difficult to get a fine balance with food ingredients alone, so if there are no additional minerals or vitamins on the list, the food may not be adequately balanced for a senior dog.

When looking at the packaging of a dog food, there will always be a section called the "guaranteed analysis." This is really helpful to use when comparing dog foods to each other. The guaranteed analysis is the percentage of protein, carbohydrates, fat, ash, moisture, and fiber which can be found in the food on an"as fed" basis. Due to this, dry food and wet food cannot be compared directly. There are some simple calculations which can be done to convert the values into a "dry matter" basis which then allows for direct comparison of the foods.

For example, if a wet food is 75% wet, then it means the dry content is 25%. If the protein level is then 5%, this can be converted by dividing by the dry matter percentage: 5/0.25 = 20% protein on a dry matter basis. Then if a similar dry food, which you wanted to compare, had a moisture content of 10% and a dry content of 90%, with a protein level of 20%, the calculation would be as follows: 20/0.9 = 22.2% protein on a dry matter basis.

A senior dog food should have an adjusted protein content of over 25% (an excellent one will have over 30%), an adjusted fat content of between 8% and 12%, and an adjusted fiber content of between 3% and 5%. Ash content (calcium, phosphorus, and magnesium) ideally should be around 2% once adjusted. Lower than 2% suggests there may not be enough minerals in the diet, and more than this suggests the diet has unnecessary filler ingredients. The guaranteed analysis sometimes also details additional ingredients such as glucosamine, omega oil, and probiotics, and generally the higher the value of these, the better. However, these are not required by the AAFCO to be included in the guaranteed analysis, so if they are not there, you cannot assume they are not in the ingredients.

Raw, BARF, and Homemade Diets

Bones and raw food diets, often referred to as BARF, have become increasingly popular in recent years, although it could be argued that rather than a recent fad, this was how dogs fed from the beginnings of time.

There are both advocates and opponents of feeding dogs raw meat and bones. Those that champion this ethos subscribe to the view that it is natural, boosts the immune system, improves digestion, preserves nutrients in their natural form, provides the dog with greater eating pleasure, and even wards off disease. Those that oppose raw feeding do so on the grounds that the diet may not be nutritionally balanced, can cause internal blockages, and is unhygienic in the home as well as a source of bacteria and parasites to the dog and people around him. Needless to say, if you choose to feed your dog a raw diet, it's important to source high quality meat and bones, and to balance the diet with vegetables and appropriate nutritional supplements.

If your dog has always been fed raw, he should be able to continue with a balanced raw diet into his senior years. This should be done through consultation with a canine nutritionist, to ensure that you are adding the appropriate minerals and vitamins for your dog's life-stage. However, if he is developing health issues such as a compromised immune system, pancreatitis, or bowel disorders, a gradual transition to a veterinary diet should be considered in consultation with your vet.

It's not advisable to switch dogs that have been fed commercial pet foods to a raw diet in the senior year. This is because the dogs have had no previous exposure to the bacteria in raw foods and have therefore not had a chance to build up immunity.

Your senior dog should never be fed table scraps, as human food is usually higher in fat, salt, sugars, artificial ingredients and other seasonings that are especially unhealthy at his life stage.

Supplements

Dog supplements, sometimes called nutraceuticals, are additional nutrients which can be added to food to improve your dog's health, especially in his senior years. About 30% of dogs receive supplements, and many more would benefit from them. However, pet supplements are not always safe. They are not regulated by the AAFCO like dog foods are, and are not required to undergo rigorous testing before they are put on the market. So, when looking into different supplements for your dog, the best ones to trust are veterinary-recommended, scientifically proven supplements, with a wealth of positive consumer reviews.

Joint Supplements

Arthritis is a common ailment which most senior dogs will end up developing to some degree. It is further discussed in Chapter 6, including the degeneration process, diagnosis, treatment and management. Arthritis is a debilitating joint condition which affects the entire joint: the cartilage, the joint lining, the joint fluid, and the subchondral bone. Trauma to the joint, as well as abnormal forces on the joint from poor conformation or excessive weight, all contribute to the development of the disease. However, joint supplements can slow the progression of the disease, as well as aid in treatment, alongside anti-inflammatories and physical therapy.

Supplements can be in the form of tablets, capsules, liquids, or pre-formulated diets. Common joint supplements include glucosamine, chondroitin, or green lipped mussel. All these have had hundreds of scientific studies which prove their effectiveness. Other popular but less researched supplements include MSM and turmeric, which also appear to be beneficial to arthritic joints. Glucosamine, chondroitin, and green lipped mussel all work by providing the building blocks of cartilage. Cartilage which has degenerated struggles to repair itself, and therefore joint supplements help to maintain the integrity of the remaining cartilage. MSM and turmeric are believed to be anti-inflammatory, and therefore they help with joint pain and reduction of inflammatory cells within the joint fluid.

Omega Oils

Omega oils can come in the form of a capsule, liquid, or as an additional ingredient to a senior dog diet. Many ingredients contain omega oils, but the most common are fish and seeds. There are three main omega oils of interest: omega-3, omega-6, and omega-9. Omega-3 and omega-6 in particular work together to have a potent impact on the body. In a ratio of between 4 and 6 omega-6 to 1 omega-3, anti-inflammatory effects are produced, which are extremely beneficial for dogs with arthritic joints. This happens by altering the chemical pathway in the area of inflammation so that the end result is less inflammation than if there were no omega oils.

Omega oils also impact the composition of the joint fluid. Joint fluid should normally be thick and viscous, allowing the joint to glide smoothly and absorb some of the concussive force. However, when a joint is arthritic, the joint fluid becomes thin and watery, which hinders it from doing its job. Omega oils improve the quality of the joint fluid so that it can provide the joint with better support and movement.

Omega oils are also extremely beneficial for coat and skin health. Older dogs tend to have thinner skin, with a duller coat. These are age-related changes. However, omega oils help build up the layer of skin to provide a better barrier to environmental attacks, as well as create a glossy smooth coat.

Mental Health Supplements

As dogs age, their mental health and or senses can deteriorate. This is a scary time for your dog, and may lead to him becoming stressed or anxious. There are several mental health supplements available to help your dog deal with the new feelings he is experiencing. These supplements usually come in the form of a tablet, chew, liquid, or food formulation. Their effects are variable, however there is plenty of excellent scientific evidence to back up how they work. These supplements have three main ingredients: L-tryptophan, casein, and dog-appeasing pheromone (DAP).

L-tryptophan increases the uptake of serotonin into the brain. Serotonin is a chemical messenger which helps your dog to experience happy feelings, thereby decreasing negative emotions. L-tryptophan has been shown to decrease dominance and territorial aggression-related behaviors, as well as improve dogs' ability to cope with stress and anxiety. This in turn can help reduce biting, barking, and destructive behaviors.

Casein can also help manage unwanted stress-related behaviors. This is a natural ingredient which is derived from a milk protein. It creates the feeling of relaxation which puppies feel when they are nursing from their mother.

Finally, DAP usually comes in the form of a diffuser or spray. DAP is a natural pheromone which dogs give off when they are relaxed, in particular from the mammary glands of mother dogs. It is odorless and cannot be sensed by humans, but dogs can sense it easily. It creates a sense of calm and relaxation, in much the same way as casein.

Probiotics

As dogs age, their guts often do not work as efficiently as they used to. Keeping your senior dog's intestines working well is vital, as not only are they responsible for absorbing all the nutrients into the blood stream, they are also one of the body's largest immune defenses. Supplementing your dog's diet with probiotics will help keep his gut healthy. These can be found added to some dog foods, but they are also available as tablets or powder which can be bought from your local pet store, veterinary clinic or online.

The gut is naturally filled with bacteria, known as flora. The bacteria which make up the flora do not harm your dog in any way. They help to digest the food so that it can be absorbed more easily into the blood stream. When your dog has a gut infection, is treated with antibiotics, or has an imbalance of this bacterial flora, harmful bacteria begin to take over. This not only damages the intestines, but also produces significant amounts of methane gas, resulting in your dog becoming bloated, uncomfortable and flatulent. Simply adding probiotics to your dog's food can prevent this from happening. This is because probiotics contain bacte-

HELPFUL TIP
Can Dogs Eat Yogurt?

The answer to the question "Can dogs eat yogurt?" is multifaceted. Yogurt is an excellent source of probiotics for humans, however, the benefits for your dog may not outweigh the risks. Older dogs often have a difficult time digesting lactose and ingesting yogurt may cause gas, diarrhea, or vomiting. It's always a good idea to discuss changes in your dog's diet with your veterinarian.

ria which are found in the flora, and therefore they improve the microenvironment of the intestines.

There are many probiotic supplements available and it can be confusing to figure out which one is the best. There are many probiotic strains, but the following have shown to have some efficacy in dogs:

- Enterococcus faecium
- Lactobacillus acidophilus
- Lactobacillus casei
- Lactobacillus plantarum
- Bifidobacterium bifidum
- Bifidobacterium animalis
- VSL#3

While human probiotics are not harmful, they will not benefit your dog, as dogs have very different gastrointestinal tracts to humans.

On the probiotic packaging, there will be a number telling you how many probiotics the product contains. A good number is above 1x108 CFU/gram. The best probiotics will also have prebiotics mixed with them, which is food for the probiotics. This works similarly to a fertilizer, and gives them energy to be as efficient as possible.

CBD Oil

CBD oil is becoming increasingly popular in the veterinary world for pain management. However, the licensing of its use in animals is a gray area. Technically, CBD oil is a supplement. It can be bought on the internet and from the shelves of pharmacies without the need for a veterinary prescription. However, you should only use it with the approval of your veterinarian, as not all dogs do well receiving CBD oil.

CBD oil is excellent for treating anxiety, stress, seizures, and cancer, but it is best at treating pain. Since many old dogs have arthritis, their days are filled with painful movements from morning to night. CBD oil is extracted from the leaves of the plant Cannabis sativa. Unlike medical and narcotic cannabis, it doesn't contain any of the psychoactive component tetrahydrocannabinol (THC), however it does contain the active component, cannabidiol, which helps lessen how much the brain perceives pain transmitted by nerve signals, such as from arthritis.

There are so many options for CBD oil on the market, and not all are suitable for dogs. Obviously, the most suitable are the ones marketed for pets, as these have been certified to be effective and completely free from THC. This is really important because otherwise your dog will feel drugged. They also come with pet-specific dosing guidelines. However, many generic CBD oils can also be used as long as you are careful about what you buy. First, always ensure the CBD oil is organic so it does not contain pesticides or additives. Generally, the higher the quality, the higher the purity and the higher the price. So, the cheapest CBD oil is unlikely to be effective. All CBD oils should be sold with a certificate of analysis, confirming exactly how much CBD a product contains and guaranteeing there is no THC present. This is particularly important, as dogs become drugged from CBD particularly easily. Finally, purchase a tincture rather than a capsule or a tablet, as it is easier to administer, and the dose can be finely adjusted. Some veterinarians will sell CBD oil, but it can also be purchased online or at a local pharmacy.

Senior Dog Feeding Guide

Not only does feeding a senior dog mean a change in food, but for some dogs, it also means a change in feeding routine and habits. Many dogs will continue as they always have, but some might become picky or have underlying health concerns which require you to change how you feed them.

While most dogs will not need to change the frequency or routine of their meals, if your dog has medications, you may find it easiest to give him his medications at the same time as he eats his meals. For example, most pain medications must be given with food to prevent gastric ulcers, and therefore, giving the medication with breakfast will help with the aches and pains your dog may feel getting up in the morning. If your dog has only ever been fed once a day in the evening, this will then need to be adjusted. Another example where the frequency of the meals may need to change is if your dog is struggling to eat large meals. He may have poor dental health, arthritis of the jaw, or possibly his cognitive function isn't what it used to be. This is an ideal time to transition to offering a little food often, such as three small meals a day, rather than one or two large ones.

Similarly, dogs may become pickier with age, resulting in large quantities of food being

FUN FACT 😀
Old Dog, New Tricks

The oldest dog to win the coveted title of Best in Show at the annual Westminster Kennel Club Dog Show was a 10-year-old Sussex spaniel called Stump. Stump's official name was Ch. Clussexx Three D Grinchy Glee but was nicknamed Stump due to his short legs and coloration which made him look like a tree trunk. Stump became the oldest dog to win the Best in Show title in 2009, replacing the previous record holder, an eight-year-old Papillon who won the title in 1999.

Photo Courtesy of
Linda Lukac

left behind. Pickiness can be related to a number of reasons. Underlying health issues should always be addressed, as major organ deterioration and pain can lead to nausea and a reduction in appetite. Poor dental health can also result in the mouth becoming painful, resulting in a reluctance to eat. Finally, with age, the senses deteriorate, which includes taste and smell. These are often the last to deteriorate, however they will still not be as sharp as they were when your dog was young. Apart from increasing the frequency of meals to improve your dog's intake, you can also make your dog's food more appetizing. Swapping to wet food, or placing a little bit of warm water on the kibble to soften it, will help your dog chew his food with less pain. Warming the food can also bring out the smell, which stimulates the senses more than usual. Finally, if this doesn't work, putting a little dog food gravy on the food or some plain chicken broth makes the food much more appetizing.

Treats also contribute to the daily calories that your dog receives, and these should be adapted for senior dogs. Dental treats are really great to help keep the teeth clean, as discussed in Chapter 4. Otherwise, treats should be kept to healthy ones only, as many commercial treats are full of calories and will undo all the hard work you've put in to feeding your dog a lower calorie senior food. Healthy treats include vegetables and fruit, such as carrots, thin apple slices without the seeds, and blueberries. Also, an excellent option is liver snaps, which can easily be made at home by dehydrating small pieces of liver in the oven.

Finally, when feeding your dog, he may appreciate the bowl being raised off the ground. Arthritis in the spine is common and may result in him having a stiff neck. A raised bowl will prevent your dog from needing to bend down to eat, and will be much more comfortable for him. Also, don't forget to frequently wash the bowls in boiling water, as they provide the perfect environment for bacteria, and elderly dogs can be much more susceptible to picking up diseases.

Importance of Weight Management

Being overweight is severely detrimental to joints of elderly dogs. As dogs age, abnormal forces on normal joints will cause arthritis to develop. Certain breeds are also prone to hip and elbow dysplasia.

As each dog is an individual, there is not an ideal weight for a small, medium, or large breed dog, so instead, weight is best measured by body condition scoring (BCS). BCS is based on a scale of 1-9, with 5 being the ideal weight, 1 is emaciated and 9 is obese.

BCS 1 = Emaciated. Ribs, lumbar vertebral projections, and bony prominences around the pelvis are clearly visible. There is severe loss of muscle and no body fat.

BCS 3 = Underweight. Ribs can be felt with ease and might be visible. Not much fat is present. The abdomen tucks up at the flank and the waist can be seen from the top. Some bony projections can be seen. It's easy to see the top of the lumbar vertebrae.

BCS 5 = Ideal. There is minimal fat over the ribs and you can easily feel them. The waist and ribs are visible when standing above the dog. The abdomen is tucked in when viewed from the side.

BCS 7 = Overweight. Fat is present over ribs and it requires some pressure to feel them. There are fat deposits over the rump and around the tail base. The waist is not easy to see. An abdominal tuck is present but slight.

BCS 9 = Obese. There's lots of fat around the base of tail, spine and chest. The abdomen may bulge behind the ribs. There's no waist or abdominal tuck. There are fat deposits on the neck and limbs.

Some dogs have a thick coat, which means the best way to measure BCS is with a hands-on approach. This way you will get a good feel for how much fat your dog has on his body. Staying in shape will be greatly beneficial to him and so if you need assistance in achieving the ideal weight, most vet practices run weight clinics with veterinary nurses to provide professional advice and support.

Diet is so closely linked to health, and by feeding your dog a balanced senior diet when he reaches his senior years, you can ensure that he has the best chance to stay as healthy as possible. Nutrition is a complicated topic, and it can seem overwhelming, but your veterinarian will be able to guide you with advice about diets, treats, and feeding practices which will be most suitable for your older dog.

CHAPTER 6
Common Senior Ailments

As discussed in Chapter 3, aging is not a disease, but a dog's body does become weaker in time, leading to increased susceptibility to certain ailments. Many of these ailments can be anticipated, and early recognition will ensure that they do not cause your older dog to become entirely debilitated. A healthy diet, plenty of exercise, and keeping your dog lean early on, will reduce the chances of many problems developing, so it is worth investing in your dog's health from a young age.

Most ailments in old age require chronic medication and management. Therefore, being prepared financially will reduce the burden of any big surprises. This may be through having pet insurance or by specifically saving up towards your dog's senior health care. Either way, elderly dogs generally have more health requirements than younger dogs, and it's important to be prepared.

An older dog can develop many ailments which can also afflict younger dogs, however there are some which are mainly just older dog problems. These are outlined in this chapter, as well as their treatment options.

Photo Courtesy of
Courtney Ryder

Photo Courtesy of Fern Connolly

Arthritis

Arthritis, also known as osteoarthritis or OA, is a degenerative disease of the joints. Sometimes just one joint is affected, and sometimes multiple joints are affected. Most dogs have some degree of arthritis in their senior years, but severe arthritis develops for only two reasons; either the joints have had abnormal forces on them over many years (for example being overweight or excessive exercise), or there have been normal forces on abnormal joints for many years (for example underlying hip dysplasia or an old cruciate ligament injury). Once arthritis begins, it cannot be reversed, however, development of the disease can certainly be slowed down with careful management.

The joint is made up of several parts; the two bones coming together, the cartilage covering the ends of the bones, and the joint fluid. When a joint has arthritis, all of the joint structures are affected. The cartilage starts to develop microscopic cracks, before completely wearing away, leaving a rough, abrasive surface on the ends of the bones when the joint moves back and forth. Underneath the cartilage, the structure of the bone changes

HELPFUL TIP
Canine Massage

If your dog suffers from arthritis, massage could be an excellent addition to his care. Canine massage promotes circulation and may relieve muscle tension, which in turn could temporarily relieve the pain and stiffness associated with arthritis. While there is no cure for arthritis, massage might improve the quality of life for your senior dog. You might choose to learn canine massage yourself, or hire a professional!

so that it cannot withstand concussive forces as well as it did in the past. Finally, the joint fluid becomes thin, so that it does not provide good lubrication to the joint in comparison to when it was more viscous.

It is estimated that at least 1 dog in 5, over the age of 8 years old, has moderate or severe arthritis. Arthritis leads to your dog being uncomfortable and moving can become hard work for him. It's likely you will only notice the condition when your dog is already in the moderate or severe category. Mild arthritis will need to be picked up by your veterinarian. The most common sign that owners notice is limping, but other symptoms can include stiffness, reluctance to go for walks, panting, and licking sore joints.

Diagnosis

Arthritis can easily be diagnosed by your vet when it is moderate or severe, however early symptoms may only be subtle. Your vet will start by looking at your dog walking and trotting to check for lameness. He will then feel all the joints while moving them to check for a creaking feeling called crepitus. He will also assess your dog's ability to flex and extend his joints to the full degree to see if your dog's range of motion is reduced.

If the vet suspects there is a problem with the joints, an x-ray will confirm whether that problem is arthritis. On an x-ray, if a joint has arthritis, it will look more fuzzy than usual, with extra boney growths, and a reduced space within the joint.

Photo Courtesy of Jessica Bimmermann

Treatment

There are many ways of treating arthritis, and a multimodal approach often yields the best results. Early arthritis can often be managed with joint supplements to improve the health of the joint, which have been discussed previously in Chapter 5.

If joint supplements are not improving the joint enough, pain relief will be required. There are many different options for pain relief, but the first-line drug that most veterinarians prescribe is called a non-steroidal anti-inflammatory drug (NSAID). This class of drugs will also lessen the inflammation in the joint, as well as improve your dog's comfort. In addition to that, other drugs can be added, such as opioids, if your dog is not entirely comfortable.

Non-medical options for pain relief may be prescribed, such as acupuncture, physiotherapy, and hydrotherapy, which are discussed in Chapter 4. These are excellent treatment options to reduce the amount of medication that your senior requires. All medication requires the liver and kidneys to work hard to filter it out of the body, so reducing the toll on these organs is always a good thing.

Additional therapies are also sometimes advised to improve your dog's comfort and joint health. CBD oil, also previously discussed in Chapter 5, is becoming popular now that it is better understood. Pentosan Polysulfate injections are also widely used. These are injections which provide components of cartilage, and therefore help to keep the structure of the cartilage as complete as possible.

Cataracts

Cataracts are structures which form in the lenses of your dog's eyes. The lenses can be found in the center of your dog's eyes, just behind the pupils. They are usually transparent, which is why the pupil looks black. Cataracts cause the lens to turn a white color, which is opaque, and once they cover the entire lens, your dog will not be able to see out of the affected eye.

Cataracts are commonly confused with nuclear sclerosis. This is a normal aging of the lens, where the fibers condense and become a gray or white color. It, however, is translucent and will not impact your dog's vision.

Cataracts can form with age, but underlying conditions often trigger them. These can be conditions such as diabetes, glaucoma (high pressure in the eye), trauma, or genetic predispositions to them.

Photo Courtesy of Nancy Walquist

Diagnosis

Cataracts can be diagnosed by your vet with a simple eye examination. He will look in your dog's eye with an ophthalmoscope, and if he cannot see to the back of the eye because the light is bouncing off the lens, then this is a positive diagnosis of a cataract. Conversely, if the light shines through the cloudiness of the lens so that he can visualize the back of the eye, this confirms that your dog has nuclear sclerosis.

Treatment

If your dog has cataracts, and he is otherwise in good health, he might be a good candidate for eye surgery. Lens replacements are possible in dogs, like humans, but it is a complicated surgery and only a specialist can do it.

If your senior has other underlying health issues which mean he is not a good candidate for surgery, unfortunately there is nothing that you can do at home to effectively slow the progression of cataracts. Some veterinarians try prescribing topical anti-inflammatories, however there has not been much evidence that these are effective.

Cancer

Everyone dreads the moment that they are told that their dog has cancer. However, there is a lot of stigma surrounding the word, and many people do not realize that cancer is not necessarily an untreatable disease.

There are many different types of cancer, and they all act differently depending on what sort of cell it originates from. Cancer is when a cell starts to divide out of control, causing a tumor to develop. Sometimes, these cells then spread to other parts of the body, such as the liver, spleen, lymph nodes, or lungs, but many tumors remain locally invasive. The tumors which spread are called malignant, and these are harder to treat, whereas the ones which stay in one place are called benign.

Diagnosis

There are many ways to diagnose cancer, but the least invasive way is for your vet to perform a fine needle aspirate. This involves inserting a needle into the tumor to remove some cells in the tip of the needle. The vet will then squirt the cells onto a slide and look at them under a microscope. Sometimes it requires a veterinary pathologist to confirm the exact type of tumor, however most vets can ascertain whether a tumor is malignant or benign from this procedure.

If your vet is concerned about the tumor, but a fine needle aspirate is inconclusive, he might opt to perform a wedge biopsy, where a small wedge shape is taken out of the tumor under sedation or anesthetic, or he might choose to completely remove the tumor and send it to a pathologist for confirmation. This will then allow him to determine whether follow up treatment is required.

FUN FACT
AKC Canine Health Foundation

The American Kennel Club Health Foundation has provided over $12 million for canine cancer research since 1995. This foundation has funded over 200 grants for cancer research and has enabled veterinarians to identify cancer at a cellular level and begin to diagnose cancer earlier. This research has contributed to human cancer research as well. As of 2020, nearly one-third of the AKC Canine Health Foundation's funds go towards researching canine cancer.

Treatment

Surgical removal of a benign tumor is usually curative, as long as the whole tumor has been removed. Your veterinarian will do this by taking out the tumor with wide margins, so that he is certain that no spreading cells are left within the body.

If the tumor is malignant, the primary tumor should be removed, and then follow-up treatment can reduce the spread of the cancer. This might be in the form of radiotherapy or chemotherapy. These treatments often concern owners, as they have many side effects, however since dogs cannot consent to the side effects, chemotherapy is not performed as aggressively as it is in humans.

Constipation

Your older dog might occasionally suffer with constipation for a couple of reasons. The most common reason is because the metabolism of older dogs slows down with age. This in turn causes a slower movement of the guts, and the food stays in the large intestine for longer. When this happens, there is more time for water absorption out of the food and into the

FUN FACT
Can My Dog Have Prunes?

If you've ever suffered from constipation, you may have gotten the recommendation to eat some prunes in order to get things moving. This may be an effective solution for humans, but is it the right approach for your dog? While consuming a prune may not be catastrophic for your canine, these dried fruits are high in sugar, which is not ideal for your dog's digestive system. If you're looking for a natural solution to occasional constipation, consider pumpkin instead of prunes.

body, causing the stools to become very hard. Another common reason for constipation is development of spondylosis. This is discussed in full later on in this chapter. Spondylosis causes the nerves in the rectum and hindquarters to become sluggish. This means squatting to defecate and pushing to pass a bowel movement becomes a challenge for your dog. This means the stools stay in the body for longer, and therefore they become harder.

Diagnosis

Diagnosis of constipation is usually made from watching your dog struggle to defecate. But sometimes an X-ray is needed to fully assess the extent of the constipation.

Treatment

Dogs can be given laxatives for constipation, much like humans. These are available from your veterinarian. If your dog is extremely constipated, he may need an enema. This is inserted into his rectum and stimulates the body to expel all the blocked-up stools.

Dementia

Dogs can suffer from a form of dementia called canine cognitive dysfunction, or CCD. This is when areas of the brain no longer work as effectively, and as a result the mental state of the dog changes.

The symptoms will differ from dog to dog, but may include tiredness, a change in personality, aimless wandering, urinating, or defecating indoors when previously housebroken, or waking up in the middle of the night and thinking it is the morning.

Diagnosis

There is no official way to diagnose CCD. However, many other ailments also have similar symptoms, so it is usually a diagnosis of exclusion. Your veterinarian is likely to perform blood and urine tests to ensure your dog's internal health is fine before coming to the conclusion that your dog has CCD.

Treatment

Some owners accept that CCD is part of aging, as it cannot be reversed. However, there are safe and effective medications which increase the blood flow to your dog's brain, and therefore also the oxygen content. This helps the cells to function more efficiently and gives your dog a new lease on life.

Dental Disease

Dental disease is a term used for the development of gingivitis and plaque build-up. Gingivitis is when the gums become extremely inflamed and reddened. This is usually in response to plaque build-up. Smaller breed dogs tend to suffer with excessive plaque on their teeth, which builds up on the base of the tooth, around the tooth-gum junction.

Plaque is a buildup of excess food material and bacteria, and can be smelly and foul tasting to your senior. This is the main cause of bad breath. When plaque is in contact with the gums, the body sends white blood cells to the area to fight the bacteria, and this in turn causes inflammation in the gums.

Most senior dogs will have dental disease to some degree, however, if you have managed your older dog's teeth effectively throughout his life, you may find that his teeth are still in a relatively functioning state. If the gingivitis becomes excessive, this weakens the ligament holding the tooth in the socket. Eventually it leads to the tooth becoming wobbly and falling out. Therefore, in addition to bad breath, you may notice your dog eating less because his mouth is sore.

Diagnosis

Dental disease can easily be detected with a dental examination. The method for this is discussed in Chapter 4. However, if your dog has severe dental disease, he may need x-rays of his mouth to understand the extent, and to determine whether any teeth need to be extracted.

Treatment

When dental disease has gone past the stage of being effectively managed with dental care, as outlined in Chapter 4, a dental procedure will be needed. Dental procedures are carried out by veterinarians under general anesthetic. Usually the procedure will only require a day visit to the vet.

Your veterinarian will start by examining all the teeth with a probe to understand which ones are loose or have pockets into the socket where the ligament is no longer effectively holding the tooth in place. These will be marked for extraction at a later part of the procedure. Next, the vet will use a scaler to remove all plaque from the outside of the teeth. Scaling the teeth will leave them pearly white again.

Once all the bacteria have been removed in the plaque, any teeth that need to be extracted are taken out. This is only done after scaling because if the mouth is full of bacteria, then bacteria can be embedded deeper in the gumline during the extraction process, which in turn can cause nasty oral infections. The extraction process can be tricky if some of the tooth is still firmly attached to the ligament, so a sharp tool, called an elevator, will be slowly run around the tooth root to weaken the ligament until it is wobbly enough to be pulled out.

Finally, the teeth are polished with an abrasive paste to ensure they are as clean as they possibly can be. This paste usually has a nice flavor to it and aids in freshening the breath of your dog.

Even though having a dental procedure may seem stressful to your older dog, the long-term benefits massively outweigh the stress. Dental disease is not pleasant, and your senior dog experiencing it is likely to have toothache and a constant foul taste in his mouth. Using routine home dental care discussed in Chapter 4, and dental procedures when needed, your dog's mouth can stay as clean and pain-free as possible.

Photo Courtesy of BrookLinn Clark

Heart Disease

Heart disease is a blanket term for any sort of degeneration of the heart. This can be for a wide variety of reasons. In small dogs, degeneration of the mitral valve (a valve in the left side of the heart to prevent backflow of blood) is usually the cause for heart disease. In larger dogs, dilated cardiomyopathy (when the heart wall thins so the pressure of the blood inside causes the heart to get bigger) is more common. Regardless of the underlying cause, the symptoms for most forms of heart disease are very similar.

The heart is the major organ for pumping blood around the body, which is essential as it carries nutrients and oxygen to the cells to produce energy. Therefore, if the blood is not reaching the cells effectively, this can cause your dog to become tired and lethargic. In extreme cases, it might also cause your dog to faint.

In late stage heart failure, your dog might cough for two reasons; firstly, when the heart becomes bigger, it pushes on a part of the lungs where there are many cough receptors. This triggers a cough. In addition to this, blood can become congested when it flows into the heart, causing fluid to leak out of the blood vessels into the lungs. This also triggers coughing and is very serious.

Diagnosis

Most heart conditions cause a heart murmur, which can be heard with a stethoscope. Heart murmurs are graded on a scale of 1 to 6. Grade 1 is when the murmur is barely audible in a quiet room, and grade 6 is when the murmur can be heard even without a stethoscope. Grades 2 to 5 are on a sliding scale of everything in between.

Once your vet has established your dog has a heart condition, the structure of the heart will need to be examined. This is done with an ultrasound machine. The direction of blood flow through the heart, and the structure of the heart muscle wall can be examined, and the exact cause of the heart condition can be established.

Treatment

Most causes of heart disease cannot be reversed, so treatment focuses on improving the pumping of the heart, as well as decreasing the congestion of blood and fluid buildup outside the heart. Drugs that cause the heart to beat stronger, decrease blood pressure, and improve fluid clearance are usually chosen as first line drugs. There are many different heart medications on the market, so often more medications are added in as the condition steadily worsens.

Kidney Failure

The kidneys play a vital role in many body systems. Their main function is to filter out waste products and excess fluid, to create urine. However, kidneys are also essential for maintaining blood pressure at a normal level.

Kidneys can function remarkably well when there is a problem, and the first signs of kidney disease only become apparent when almost 70% of the kidneys are destroyed. Symptoms of kidney disease include drinking more, urinating more, losing weight, decreased appetite, vomiting, foul breath, and sometimes mouth ulcers.

Diagnosis

Kidney disease is usually diagnosed with a blood test and urine test. This looks at how well the kidneys are functioning and the degree of damage. The blood test will give values of urea and creatinine, which when elevated indicates the kidneys are not functioning well. Early kidney disease blood tests can be done to assess early warning sign for impending kidney problems.

Treatment

There is no treatment for the reversal of kidney disease, however many things can be done to slow down the progression of the disease. First, a veterinary kidney diet will help the kidneys not to be overloaded with protein, which can worsen their inflammation. All dog patients with kidney disease should immediately have their diets changed to this. Kidney diets also have lower levels of phosphate, which can increase in the blood at this time, as the kidneys are not filtering it out effectively.

Kidney medication aims to normalize blood pressure and improve the filtration of the kidneys. This in turn helps regulate the blood flow through the kidneys, slowing down the damage. Some kidney medications are the same as heart medications, as they aim to improve blood flow and alleviate congestion.

Liver Failure

The liver is an essential organ that works alongside the kidneys to filter out waste products from the body. But it also has many other functions. It metabolizes food and medications, to make sure they are in usable forms. It also produces bile, which is excreted into the intestine to help digest fats. Therefore, if the liver is not functioning well, this is very serious.

Liver failure in older dogs can occur for a number of reasons. The most common reasons include fibrosis or scarring, cancer, and adverse effects from chronic medication.

The symptoms of liver failure are usually relatively generic. Vomiting and lethargy are common symptoms. In severe cases, your dog may be jaundiced, seen as a yellow tinge to his gums. This is because the liver filters bilirubin, but if there is a backlog of bilirubin into the liver, it creates a yellow color. Finally, in some cases, your dog may become spaced out or have neurological symptoms, like seizures and pressing his head against walls. This is from a build-up of ammonia in the blood, due to too much protein.

Diagnosis

As with the kidneys, blood tests can be run to measure the levels of the liver enzymes. If these are raised, then there is damage to the liver cells.

The liver can be examined with an ultrasound machine, but unless it has obvious tumors protruding from it, the underlying cause can be difficult to ascertain without taking a biopsy. A biopsy requires a long needle to be carefully inserted into the liver under sedation. It does not come without risks, as there are many organs in that area, and the insertion of the needle can cause bleeding. In addition, some older dogs are not suitable candidates for sedation. For these reasons, some people choose not to pursue further diagnostics. However, if your senior is in otherwise good health, then a biopsy will help you understand the problem and the best way to treat it.

Treatment

Treatment for liver failure is mainly supportive, unless there is a tumor which can be surgically removed. A veterinary liver support diet will help provide the nutrients needed without too much protein, which can put strain on the liver. Liver support supplements, such as SAM-e, can also be provided by your vet to help with the function of your dog's liver.

If your dog is experiencing neurological symptoms, your vet may prescribe lactulose. This helps reduce the amount of ammonia absorbed from the guts after a meal.

Prostatic Enlargement

Prostatic enlargement is a common scenario for elderly male dogs which have not been sterilized earlier in life. It can be either cancerous or benign, so it's important to have it checked. Most times it is benign and can be treated.

Even if the enlargement is benign, it can still have a major effect on your dog. The prostate sits close to the rectum, which can become compressed if it is enlarged, leading to difficulty defecating. Likewise, the urethra runs through it, meaning that enlargement can also cause difficulty urinating. In severe cases, particularly in cases of cancerous enlargement, it can affect the spinal cord which is located just above it, resulting in problems with the back legs.

Diagnosis

If you suspect your dog has prostatic enlargement, you can ask your vet to check it. He does this with a rectal examination, where he places a finger inside to check how enlarged the prostate is. Your dog may resent it, but it is important to know whether it is causing a problem.

Diagnostic imaging, such as ultrasound or x-rays can also help diagnose prostatic enlargement, as there are many other ailments that cause similar symptoms, and checking the whole area is important to make sure nothing is missed.

Treatment

Treatment for prostatic enlargement starts with castration. Hormones have a large impact on the prostate, and therefore removing the hormones usually causes the enlargement to lessen. In dogs where surgery is not an option, or the rare cases where they are already castrated, a drug called delmadinone can be used to suppress growth.

If your dog is struggling to urinate or defecate, then this condition needs to be treated symptomatically. Medications can be given to soften the stools, which helps them to pass through the smaller space. If your dog cannot urinate at all, he will need to have a catheter passed to keep open the passage of the urethra through the prostate.

Pyometra

Pyometra is a disease of unspayed females, where the uterus becomes infected and fills with pus. It commonly happens in older female dogs; however, any age female dog can develop pyometra if she has not been spayed. This is one of the driving factors for spaying female dogs.

Pyometras can be life-threatening, particularly in older dogs. There are two types of pyometra; open and closed. Open pyometras are when the cervix is open and pus drains out the vagina. Closed pyometras are very dangerous, as the cervix is closed and the pus builds up inside. This can lead to uterine rupture which is almost always fatal.

Symptoms can be variable. The most common symptom is simply being off-color. It is sometimes accompanied by urinating and drinking more, vomiting, vaginal discharge, lack of appetite, and a high temperature. Another clue is when these symptoms develop within three months of your dog being in estrus.

Diagnosis

Your vet will usually be able to diagnose your dog with pyometra relatively easily, with a clinical examination, history, and blood test showing a high white blood cell count. However, a definitive test requires an ultrasound or x-ray to see that the uterus is enlarged.

Treatment

The ideal treatment for pyometra is surgical removal of the uterus, especially if the pyometra is closed. Time is of the essence, if you wait to see if it improves, the uterus can rupture. If it is a pyometra which is draining, and your dog seems relatively bright and well, your dog can be initially be treated medically before surgery with very careful monitoring by your veterinarian. This involves being given antibiotics, hormones, and fluid therapy. This usually allows the uterus to expel all the infection and return to a normal size. Your dog will still need surgery, as without surgery the condition will reoccur, but by treating medically first, your dog will be at much less risk under anesthetic compared to if she was unwell.

Spondylosis

Spondylosis deformans is a degenerative spinal condition, where bone spurs develop under the vertebrae. Sometimes this is as a result of injury or repetitive stress, however it can also happen with no inciting cause. Larger dogs are more at risk, but any dog can develop it in old age.

Most bone spurs develop over the chest or in the lower spine just before the pelvis. Small spurs won't cause your dog any problems, but as they grow, they can cause nerve damage, mobility issues, and considerable pain. Typical symptoms involve back spasms when pressure is applied to a dog's back, stiffness, lack of flexibility, limping, scuffing the back paws when walking, and difficulty squatting to defecate. Because your dog may not wish to defecate due to the pain, secondary constipation can develop.

Diagnosis

Your veterinarian can perform a clinical examination to investigate whether your dog is uncomfortable in his back, however the only way to fully understand the extent of the spondylosis requires an x-ray to visualize the bone spurs.

Treatment

Surgery is not usually an option to remove the bone spurs as operating on the spine is extremely difficult. Most dogs require anti-inflammatories to control the discomfort. The immobility and pain can also be controlled with physical therapies such as physiotherapy, hydrotherapy and acupuncture, as discussed in Chapter 4.

Weight also puts more stress on the back, so if your dog is overweight, he will benefit from going on a diet. Sometimes weight loss is all that is needed to give him some relief.

Urinary Incontinence

Urinary incontinence in older dogs is commonly due to a condition called "urinary sphincter mechanism incontinence" or USMI. This develops in female dogs who have been spayed, usually before their first estrus.

The hormone estrogen helps to tighten up the muscular band at the exit of the bladder, known as the urinary sphincter. When a dog hasn't had any estrogen in their body for a lifetime, it causes the sphincter to become leaky, especially when pressure is put on it from a full bladder. As a result, leaking most often happens when your dog lies down or makes a sudden movement, such as jumping. It causes no concern to her, and is not painful as long as the urine does not cause the skin to develop urine scald down the back legs, however it often causes a lot of distress to owners, as furniture and carpets get urine on them.

Diagnosis

There isn't a specific diagnostic procedure which diagnoses USMI, but instead it is usually a diagnosis of exclusion. Your vet is likely to perform a blood and urine test to make sure the kidneys are not the problem. USMI responds very well to treatment, so if there is no improvement, then this is also usually a clue that the diagnosis is incorrect.

Treatment

USMI can be treated by two means; a syrup which improves the tone of the urinary sphincter or tablets which replace the estrogen in the body. Both are usually very effective, but certain dogs respond better to one over the other, so your vet may try one treatment, then switch to the other to see which is the best.

***

While it may seem that older dogs are more susceptible to ailments, this is not necessarily the case. Instead, different life stages are prone to different ailments. So being prepared for what an older dog may develop will help you catch it early, to ensure your senior dog gets immediate treatment and end up with the best outcome.

CHAPTER 7
Saying Goodbye

Photo Courtesy of
Renee' Willard

Saying goodbye to your dog is never easy, but inevitably that day will come. Being prepared for what to expect may help you feel more at peace about the process. Nevertheless, it is only natural for questions to arise such as, "Will it hurt?", "Can it be done at home?", and "Can I be present during it?" This chapter aims to answer all these questions, so that you know the facts and can be ready when the time comes.

When is it Time?

The phrase which is commonly used by veterinarians is "quality of life." This is a marker of whether or not your senior is still enjoying life without suffering. There is no official measure for quality of life, but most veterinarians interpret it in the following ways:

- Your dog is mobile, and can get up, walk, and sit down without excessive discomfort.

- Your dog still wants to interact, and enjoys his time with you.

- Your dog still wants to eat.

- Your dog still wags his tail.

- Your dog is not considered to be suffering excessively from any disease.

You know your dog better than anyone, so you are the best person to judge all of the above points. But your veterinarian will help guide you in the decision-making process if you are not sure. Unfortunately, most dogs do not come to a day where they suddenly collapse and make the decision for you. Most dogs go through a gray area, and grumble on with their problems for a while, making it difficult to decide if it's time. Generally, a good approach to take is it's better one day too early, than one day too late so your dog endures unnecessary suffering.

One thing which is important to remember is that dogs do not have the ability to worry about the future. He does not worry about what is to come, and therefore cannot worry about passing away. This is something which only humans have the ability to do. All your dog is concerned with is how he is feeling at a given point in time, and if his quality of life is poor, that is what he is concerned about. Therefore, try not to worry your dog by being anxious around him about what is to come, as he will not understand this. Many people find peace in the knowledge that dogs cannot worry about death.

Understanding the Euthanasia Process

If you don't know what is going to happen in a euthanasia procedure, it can be a time which will fill you with great anxiety. Most vets will explain everything to you before it happens, but being prepared may give you some peace.

Euthanasia is completely humane. It does not hurt, and your dog does not know what is about to happen, and therefore cannot worry about it. However, if you act anxious, then your dog will pick up on this and feel anxious himself.

The procedure can take place either at your veterinary clinic or at home. If you choose to take your dog to the vet, bring something comfortable with you which he is familiar with, whether that is your dog's bed, a blanket, or a pillow. This will help soothe him.

It can sometimes be difficult to stay with your dog and see everything, however if you can, it is best for him. His last few moments shouldn't be in an unfamiliar place with unfamiliar people. However, if you feel personally unable to be with your dog at the end, you may find that a good friend who your dog knows and loves will be willing to step in. Your vet might start by giving your dog an injection of sedative. Not all veterinarians will sedate dogs beforehand, but it is common practice if your dog is frightened, aggressive, or can't relax. You can always ask to have your dog sedated, even if he is calm.

Once he is sedated, your vet will place a catheter into the vein in your dog's front leg, so that he has access to the vein. He will administer a medication called phenobarbital, which is a seizure medication that is similar to an anesthetic. It works very quickly, and in most cases will shut down the heart and brain within thirty seconds to one minute.

When your pet passes away, you might see a few things that could startle you, so knowing about them beforehand is important. Your dog's eyes are unlikely to fully close, and he may urinate or defecate as all his

Photo Courtesy of Gail Krenn

muscles relax. There may also be twitching in some muscles, and in some cases, a deep inhaled breath can happen. This does not mean your dog is still alive, but it can occur as the muscles shut down.

Afterwards, you have several options. Some people choose to take their dog home to be buried, and if this is what you would like to do, it is a good idea to line the back of your car with towels in case any bodily fluids leak out on your journey home. Most vets can also offer cremation, where you can either have the ashes returned to sprinkle somewhere yourself, or have them sprinkled at the pet crematorium.

Many owners find comfort in having some of their pet's ashes made into jewelry, and companies that offer this service may be found on the internet. Other commemoration jewelry may hold a small piece of your dog's hair. If this is something that may appeal to you, you should take a small clipping of hair before laying your dog to rest.

Talking to Children

Talking to children about euthanasia can be one of the hardest facts of life to explain. Often the passing of a family dog is the first time a child has dealt with death, and therefore how the event is handled will impact their understanding about dying in the future.

Many children, particularly younger ones, do not understand that a dog's biological clock is different to that of a human, and therefore they think that their relationship is indefinite. Regardless of how old your child is, honesty is the best policy. Using the words 'death' or 'dying' is important, as otherwise your child might not fully understand what you are trying to say. Using the term 'put to sleep' can be confusing, and if your child is young, they might suffer extreme anxiety if you bury your dog, and he believes he is just sleeping. You should also explain what the term 'dying' means. Explain that your dog's body is no longer working, and if you have religious beliefs, your child might understand the concept of a soul. Explaining the permanence of death is also needed, but all of this must be done in a gentle way.

If your child asks questions about the process, you should make sure you give him plenty of time to ask them, and answer them as honestly as possible. Some children might also want to be present, however it depends on your child's age and maturity.

Once your dog has been euthanized, it can be a good idea to hold a memorial service with your children. Encourage them to express their feelings about him, by either talking or writing about the best times they had with their dog. This is also a good opportunity for you to express your feelings, so that your children know that they are not alone in their grief.

Depending on the age of your child, your child is likely to react in different ways:

Under 2: Your child is likely to respond to the death of your dog based on how you react. If you are stressed about it, your child will be stressed.

2 to 5: Your child is likely to miss his playmate. He may think that death is only temporary, much like how leaves fall off a tree and regrow in a different season. Often there is a temporary regress in coping behaviors such as becoming more needy or sucking their thumb.

5 to 9: At this age, most children understand that death is permanent, but might think that bargaining can save their dog. This is also the age when children might feel guilty after their pet dies, and so it is important to reassure your child that they didn't cause their dog's death.

Older than 10: Children in this age range understand that all living creatures will eventually die, and that it is permanent, however they can't always accept it as easily as an adult can. It is likely they will go through the stages of grief that an adult would, which are discussed next.

Dealing with Grief

Coping with the death of your long-term companion can be painful, and it is normal to grieve. But understanding and recognizing the steps of grief can help you map out your path to resolution. However, grief is different for every individual, and the process of grief has no 'normal' time period.

There are six stages of grief which usually come in a set order:

1. Denial: You may experience a time of denial as it can be difficult to accept that your dog has died or is dying. It can be a particularly strong feeling if your dog has suddenly died.

2. Bargaining: It is not uncommon to try to bargain a deal with yourself or God to attempt to avoid fate.

Photo Courtesy of
Kayla Stilger

3. Anger: As you will probably feel many strong emotions, it is easy for them to come out as anger, particularly to those who were close to your oldie such as family, your vet or even yourself.

4. Guilt: Out of all the stages, most people will go through a stage of guilt after their dog passes, particularly about decisions made regarding the care of the dog in its last stage of life. It is important to remember you always put your dog's best interest first, and not to doubt your decisions.

5. Depression: When you reach the stage of depression, you are close to accepting that your pet has passed away. You might feel you want to be alone during this stage, but it is important to seek help if you feel overwhelmed with this feeling. You will find much empathy from anyone who has also suffered the loss of a dog. Or you may find comfort from a professional pet bereavement counselor.

6. Acceptance: This is a really important stage. This is when each day it becomes a little bit easier to think of your dog. You can start to look at daily reminders of your senior with fondness and good memories, rather than sadness.

Grief isn't easy, and it shouldn't be. If you feel grief, then it highlights how important your dog was to you. Acknowledging and recognizing the stages will help you deal with your grief, and remembering it will pass in time should be a comfort. Remember that if you feel overwhelmed, do not stay quiet and seek help, whether that be from friends, family or professional help.

Rainbow Bridge Poem

A popular poem, called Rainbow Bridge, might help you find comfort after the loss of your old companion:

There is a bridge connecting Heaven and Earth.

It is called the Rainbow Bridge because of all its beautiful colors.

Just this side of the Rainbow Bridge there is a land of meadows,

hills and valleys with lush green grass.

When a beloved pet dies, the pet goes to this place.

There is always food and water and warm spring weather.

The old and frail animals are young again.

Those who were sick, hurt or in pain are made whole again.

There is only one thing missing,

they are not with their special person who loved them so much on earth.

So each day they run and play until the day comes

when one suddenly stops playing and looks up!

The nose twitches! The ears are up!

The eyes are staring and this one runs from the group!

You have been seen and when you and your special friend meet,

you take him in your arms and hug him.

He licks and kisses your face again and again -

and you look once more into the eyes of your best friend and trusting pet.

Then you cross the Rainbow Bridge together never again to be apart.

Author: unknown

Acknowledgements

I'd like to extend my thanks to Clare Hardy, who is has been a huge support throughout my writing career. From the very start, she has worked with me as an editor, and her contributions have always been very valuable. Even though it has now been many years since the first book I ever published, I still learn from her every day, and I'm truly grateful for her input.

I would also like to thank my clients. In my line of work, I see many elderly dogs, and so I'm grateful that my clients trust me with their dogs in their final fragile years. I hope that this book can be a valuable guide to people with older dogs, so that I can help more people that are on a journey into their dog's senior years.

Printed in Great Britain
by Amazon

56884508R00061